Workbook for

LEADERSHIP & PROBLEM SOLVING

 MILITARY SCIENCE AND LEADERSHIP   MSL 301

Edited by

Sheila Visconti

McGraw-Hill Primis
Custom Publishing

Boston   Burr Ridge, IL   Dubuque, IA   Madison, WI   New York   San Francisco   St. Louis
Bangkok   Bogotá   Caracas   Lisbon   London   Madrid
Mexico City   Milan   New Delhi   Seoul   Singapore   Sydney   Taipei   Toronto

McGraw-Hill Higher Education
A Division of The **McGraw-Hill** Companies

Workbook for
LEADERSHIP & PROBLEM SOLVING
Military Science and Leadership
MSL 301

McGraw-Hill's Primis Custom Publishing consists of products that are produced from camera-ready copy. Peer review, class testing, and accuracy are primarily the responsibility of the author(s).

3 4 5 6 7 8 9 0 QPD QPD 0 9 8 7 6 5 4 3

ISBN 0-07-284060-9

Sponsoring Editor: Judy A. Wetherington
Production Editor: Carrie Braun
Cover Design: Fairfax Hutter
Printer/Binder: Quebecor World

CONTENTS

INTRODUCTION

OVERVIEW OF THE ARMY ROTC ADVANCED COURSE

The Army ROTC Advanced Course is comprised of four courses, Military Science and Leadership (MSL) 301, MSL 302, MSL 401, and MSL 402 and the National Advanced Leadership Camp (NALC). The Advanced Course is designed to teach all knowledge, skills, and attitudes essential for commissioning as a new second lieutenant, and to establish a sound foundation for a career as a commissioned Army officer. The content and methods of the Advanced Course assume no prior cadet experience or other military training. This approach is taken because the Advanced Course comprises the minimum curriculum that an individual must complete in order to be commissioned.

Advanced Course lessons are carefully sequenced, linked, and progressive in their treatment of key officer knowledge and competencies. Students are encouraged to synthesize lessons to form broader perspectives, deeper insights, and more robust problem-solving abilities, by the use of case studies and simulations that require the use of skills and knowledge learned in a wide variety of earlier lessons. The sequencing of lessons is also designed to meet the immediate needs of cadets by addressing topics needed for success in the performance of cadet responsibilities early in the MSL 301 term, and at the NALC, and topics designed to facilitate entry into active military service during the MSL 402 term.

OVERVIEW OF THE MSL 301 COURSE: LEADERSHIP & PROBLEM SOLVING

The MSL 301 course is designed to enable a student with no prior military or cadet experience to quickly learn essential cadet knowledge and skills necessary for integration into the cadet battalion and successful performance of key cadet tasks. First you will be introduced to principles of physical fitness and healthy lifestyle so that you may effectively work to improve or maintain your physical fitness from the very beginning of the term. Next, you will be introduced to the Leader Development Program that will be used to evaluate your leadership performance and provide you developmental feedback for the rest of your cadet years. To help prepare you for their responsibilities in teaching and participating in Military Science and

Leadership Labs, you will then be taught how to plan and conduct individual and small unit training, as well as basic tactical principles. Following these important introductory modules, the course turns to a four-week study of reasoning skills and the military-specific application of these skills in the form of the Army's troop leading procedure. The term concludes its final four weeks with a detailed examination of officership, which culminates in a five-hour officership case study. This treatment of officership is especially appropriate in this term because MSL 301 is the first term that *all* cadets, regardless of your route of entry into ROTC, must take.

COURSE STRUCTURE: A MODULAR APPROACH

This course is structured in modules and lessons. There are five modules containing 36 one-hour (50 minute) lessons as follows:

MODULE	TRACK
Module I	Physical Well-being (Lessons 1–3)
Module II	Personal Development (Lessons 4, 5 and 13–16)
Module III	The Army Profession: Army Operations (Lessons 6–12 and 17–24)
Module IV	The Army Profession: Officership (Lessons 25–36)

In addition, Leadership Labs that provide practical experience are scheduled during each semester. Leadership Labs meet a minimum of 1 hour per week.

HOW TO USE THIS TEXT

This textbook is divided by sections/modules, and is organized according to the Cadet Command class schedule model. Scope statements for each module are found on the module title pages. Within each module is a series of lessons that support the module. Each lesson begins with a purpose statement and a list of topics covered by the lesson, followed by the learning objectives identified for that lesson and a cadet checklist to guide you when preparing for class.

WHAT IS EXPERIENTIAL LEARNING?

Experiential learning simply means learning from an experience.

When participants are provided the opportunity to "experience" their learning rather than being told what they are to learn, experiential learning is taking place. Experiential Learning is rewarding, yet demanding, for both learners and teachers because the learning takes place during class as much as it does outside the classroom, from unstructured as well as structured experiences. Experiential learning is founded on the belief that interaction is central to the learning process: cadet/faculty interaction, cadet/cadet interaction, and cadet/instructional material.

Helpful synonyms are: direct experience, discovery learning, experience-based learning, action learning, active learning, and participatory learning.

THE CADET COMMAND APPROACH TO ACADEMIC INSTRUCTION

The Military Science and Leadership program is designed to focus on the student (cadet), rather than the instructor or the subject matter. Focusing on the cadet requires student-centered objectives and conscious attention to how cadets react to the instruction received. For effective instruction, students need feedback that reinforces learning while identifying and correcting errors. Students need the opportunity to try to work with what has been taught. Too often instruction is limited to the delivery of information, either through reading assignments, lectures, or slide presentations.

Typically, we think of successful experiential learning as consisting of five steps:

1. Readiness/openness to the experience
2. The experience itself
3. Reflection upon the experience
4. Analysis, theory or additional information to clarify the relationship between theory and actions, with an understanding of lessons learned regarding any needed changes
5. The opportunity to re-experience (practice in new situations/practical exercises)

STUDENT RESOURCES

a. *Cadet text.* The Cadet text contains the readings that support the MSL 301 course: Leadership and Problem Solving.
b. *Cadet CD-ROM.* A CD-ROM is included in each cadet textbook and contains additional reference materials, readings and multimedia that support the MSL program.
c. *Cadet Workbook.* Packaged with cadet text of readings, this workbook contains the worksheets that support the exercises woven throughout the course. In addition, the workbook contains checklists and lesson overview statements for use by the cadet when preparing for class.
d. *Blackboard (Bb).* The Blackboard course site, *http://rotc.blackboard.com,* contains Military Science and Leadership course materials.

FORMAT OF LESSON PLANS:

This is an example of a cadet's lesson plan describing the general content of each field.

1	**Lesson Number**	Standardizes assigned lesson number.
2	**Lesson Title**	Standardized assigned lesson title.
3	**Revision Date**	Date last revised.
4	**Term**	Semester or quarter lesson is taught.
5	**Cadet Prep Time**	Time needed for preparation in and outside of class.
6	**Prerequisite lesson(s)**	List of any courses or activities required before taking class.
7	**Lesson Overview**	A brief description of the lesson's:
		■ **Context** ■ **Purpose** ■ **Prior class activities** ■ **In class activities** and ■ **Cadet's learning experiences.** This section states the lesson goal, its relationship to the track and over-all curriculum, details of the types of activities to be used and how these activities will produce the desired outcome.
8	Lesson Activities	Time, types and sequence of lesson activities to include: lesson:
		■ **Introduction** ■ **Pre-class activities** ■ **Set up** ■ **Lesson conclusion** and ■ **Requirements for the next lesson.**
9	Cadet Readings	A complete listing of **required** and **optional readings.**
10	Cadet Checklist	A **checklist** of the steps to follow, materials needed and time required preparing for the class.
11	Objectives	A list of Learning Objectives to be met by the cadet that will "enable" the cadet to reach the overall objective(s) of the lesson. These objectives are observable, measurable, and they will be used to evaluate the lesson and cadet's progress.

MODULE I

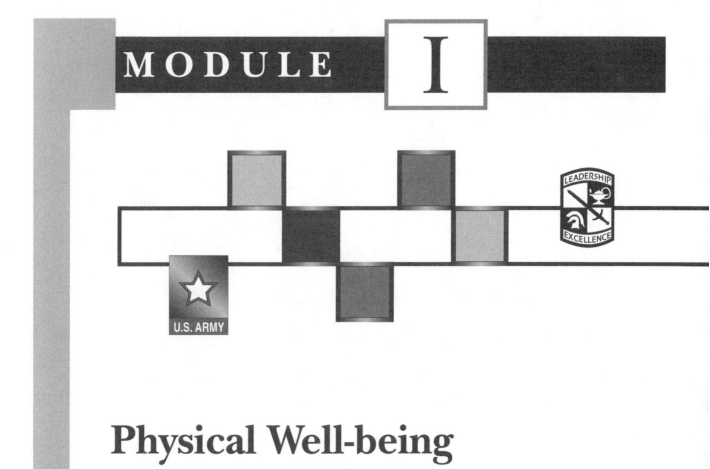

Physical Well-being

The Physical Well-being module is comprised of three lessons designed to introduce you to the standards of fitness that will be expected of you and to provide basic principles of fitness and diet that support a healthy lifestyle. Lesson one sets the tone for the importance of physical well-being as essential to the profession of the Army. The second lesson in the Physical Well-being module focuses on wellness while the third lesson emphasizes nutrition. Combined, these three lessons give you what you need to build and implement a total physical fitness program. The ultimate goal is you will willingly pursue a healthy lifestyle including a diet and fitness plan designed to achieve Army standards and individually established fitness goals.

Physical Fitness and Bearing

This lesson is intended to accomplish the following: raise your awareness of the Army's physical fitness requirements; relate personal assessment to physical wellness; and, provide a set of tools for you to use to monitor and to improve your own physical fitness.

The following topics are addressed in this lesson:

- Fitness components
- Principle of exercise
- Personal responsibility for fitness

The following Terminal Learning Objective (TLO) is supported in whole or in part by this lesson:

- Implement a Total Fitness Program

Following this lesson you will be able to:

- Describe the components of fitness as they relate to the Army's APFT
- Assess current health status
- Assess methods for improving physical health
- Explain the physical and emotional aspects of bearing as it relates to leadership

CADET CHECKLIST

This is the first lesson. The average time for pre-class activity is about 30 min. or less.

___ Go to Blackboard course site for MSL301-Lesson 01 and preview the lesson.

___ Review the materials in your Workbook and skim the online readings:

    ___ 1. Review the *HOOAH4You* resources list. This pull down menu box is located on the opening page of the website: http://hooah4health.com/4You/default.htm

    ___ 2. Preview the *Improving Physical Fitness* worksheet.

    ___ 3. Preview the *How Healthy Are You?* Worksheet.

___ In preparation for the **next** class (MSL301-Lesson 02) you will need to complete the interactive online Health Goals Checklist and print out the results. *http://www.hooah4health.com/body/fitguard/default.htm*

___ In preparation for the **next** class (MSL301-Lesson 02) you will need to fill out the Physical Fitness Log for one day.

OPTIONAL

    ___ 1. Fill out the *"Fit to Win"* Self-Test for Better Health Scorecard in DA PAM 600-63-14 Your *"Fit to Win"* Handbook. This is located on the accompanying Cadet CD-ROM.

Name _____   Date _____

PHYSICAL FITNESS LOG

Name (Last)	First	MI			Rank	Sex (Circle) M F	Organization		
Week	Date	Phase of Training	Exercise Activity No. 1	Reps, Time, Distance, Etc.	Heart Rate Attained	Exercise Activity No. 2	Reps, Time, Distance, Etc.	Heart Rate Attained

INSRUCTIONS: 1. Record each worout by entry of date, phase of training, activityies performed, and heart rate attained. Also indicate the repetitions, time, or other indication of performance for each activity in the block provided. 2. At the end of each week, extend the last horizontal line to the left to indicate the end of the week, and place the number of the week in the weekly column.

FM 21-20, Appendix C

1	**Exercise Title**	Improving Physical Fitness
2	**Exercise Number**	MSL301_L01_02C
3	**Type**	Worksheet
4	**Notes**	
5	**Purpose**	Relate personal fitness goals to Army requirements. Recognize successes and paths to improving physical fitness.
6	**Directions**	

Do you smoke? Are you overweight? Do you exercise regularly? Do you eat a low-fat diet? Do you feel good about how you take care of yourself? Do you have a lifestyle that promotes physical and mental wellness?

Respond thoughtfully to each of the questions listed below.

Questions:

1. List three examples of changes you could make in order to improve your fitness.

    _____

    _____

    _____

2. Select one improvement. How could you achieve and maintain that change?

    _____

    _____

    _____

    _____

    _____

3a. Identify a physical fitness goal that you have not yet achieved.

    _____

    _____

    _____

3b. What will it take to achieve that goal?

    _____

    _____

    _____

1	**Exercise Title**	How Healthy Are You?
2	**Exercise Number**	MSL301_L01_03C
3	**Type**	Worksheet
4	**Notes**	
5	**Purpose**	Self-assessment to allow cadets to determine their personal wellness.

6	**Directions**

Although many of us recognize the importance of healthy behaviors, we are often negligent in maintaining a health regimen. Rate your health status in each of the following dimensions by circling the number that best describes you.

1. Very Unhealthy
2. Somewhat Unhealthy
3. Somewhat Healthy
4. Very Healthy

Physical Health

1
2
3
4

Social Health

1
2
3
4

Emotional Health

1
2
3
4

Environmental Health

1
2
3
4

Spiritual Health

1
2
3
4

Intellectual Health

1
2
3
4

After completing the above section, how healthy do you think you are? Which area(s), if any, should you work on improving?

Now answer the following set of questions regarding each dimension of health. Indicate how often you think the statements describe you.

Physical Health

	Rarely, If Ever	Sometimes	Most of the Time	Always
1. I maintain a desirable weight.	1	2	3	4
2. I engage in vigorous exercises such as brisk walking, jogging, swimming, or running for at least 30 minutes per day, 3-4 times per week.	1	2	3	4
3. I do exercises designed to strengthen my muscles and joints.	1	2	3	4
4. I warm up and cool down by stretching before and after vigorous exercise.	1	2	3	4
5. I feel good about the condition of my body.	1	2	3	4
6. I get 7-8 hours of sleep each night.	1	2	3	4
7. My immune system is strong and I am able to avoid most infectious diseases.	1	2	3	4
8. My body heals itself quickly when I get sick or injured.	1	2	3	4
9. I have lots of energy and can get through the day without being overly tired.	1	2	3	4
10. I listen to my body; when there is something wrong, I seek professional advice.	1	2	3	4

Social Health

	Rarely, If Ever	Sometimes	Most of the Time	Always
1. When I meet people, I feel good about the impression I make on them.	1	2	3	4
2. I am open, honest, and get along well with other people.	1	2	3	4
3. I participate in a wide variety of social activities and enjoy being with people who are different from me.	1	2	3	4
4. I try to be a "better person" and work on behaviors that have caused problems in my interactions with others.	1	2	3	4
5. I get along well with the members of my family.	1	2	3	4
6. I am a good listener.	1	2	3	4
7. I am open and accessible to a loving and responsible relationship.	1	2	3	4
8. I have someone I can talk to about my private feelings.	1	2	3	4
9. I consider the feeling of others and do not act in hurtful or selfish ways.	1	2	3	4
10. I consider how what I say might be perceived by others before I speak.	1	2	3	4

Emotional Health

	Rarely, If Ever	Sometimes	Most of the Time	Always
1. I find it easy to laugh about things that happen in my life.	1	2	3	4
2. I avoid using alcohol as a means of helping me forget my problems.	1	2	3	4
3. I can express my feelings without feeling silly.	1	2	3	4
4. When I am angry, I try to let others know in nonconfrontational and nonhurtful ways.	1	2	3	4
5. I am not a chronic worrier and do not tend to be suspicious of others.	1	2	3	4
6. I recognize when I am stressed and take steps to relax through exercise, quiet time, or other activities.	1	2	3	4
7. I feel good about myself and believe others like me for who I am.	1	2	3	4
8. When I am upset, I talk to others and actively try to work through my problems.	1	2	3	4
9. I am flexible and adapt or adjust to change in a positive way.	1	2	3	4
10. My friends regard me as a stable, emotionally well adjusted person.	1	2	3	4

Environmental Health

	Rarely, If Ever	Sometimes	Most of the Time	Always
1. I am concerned about environmental pollution and actively try to preserve and protect natural resources.	1	2	3	4
2. I report people who intentionally hurt the environment.	1	2	3	4
3. I recycle my garbage.	1	2	3	4
4. I reuse plastic and paper bags and tin foil.	1	2	3	4
5. I vote for pro-environment candidates in elections.	1	2	3	4
6. I write my elected leaders about environmental concerns.	1	2	3	4
7. I consider the amount of packaging covering a product when I buy groceries.	1	2	3	4
8. I try to buy products that are recyclable.	1	2	3	4
9. I use both sides of the paper when taking class notes or doing assignments.	1	2	3	4
10. I try not to leave the faucet running too long when I brush my teeth, shave, or bathe.	1	2	3	4

Spiritual Health

	Rarely, If Ever	Sometimes	Most of the Time	Always
1. I believe life is a precious gift that should be nurtured.	1	2	3	4
2. I take time to enjoy nature and the beauty around me.	1	2	3	4
3. I take time alone to think about what's important in life - who I am, what I value, where I fit in, and where I'm going.	1	2	3	4
4. I have faith in a greater power, be it a God-like force, nature, or the connectedness of all living things.	1	2	3	4
5. I engage in acts of caring and good will without expecting something in return.	1	2	3	4
6. I feel sorrow for those who are suffering and try to help them through difficult times.	1	2	3	4
7. I feel confident that I have touched the lives of others in a positive way.	1	2	3	4
8. I work for peace in my interpersonal relationships, in my community, and in the world at large.	1	2	3	4
9. I am content with who I am.	1	2	3	4
10. I go for the gusto and experience life to the fullest.	1	2	3	4

Intellectual Health

	Rarely, If Ever	Sometimes	Most of the Time	Always
1. I think about consequences before I act.	4	3	2	1
2. I learn from my mistakes and try to act differently the next time.	1	2	3	4
3. I follow directions or recommended guidelines and act in ways likely to keep myself and others safe.	1	2	3	4
4. I consider the alternatives before making decisions.	1	2	3	4
5. I am alert and ready to respond to life's challenges in ways that reflect thought and sound judgment.	1	2	3	4
6. I tend to let my emotions get the better of me and I act without thinking.	4	3	2	1
7. I actively learn all I can about products and services before making decisions.	1	2	3	4
8. I manage my time well rather than let time manage me.	1	2	3	4
9. My friends and family trust my judgment.	1	2	3	4
10. I think about my self-talk (the things I tell myself) and then examine the evidence to see if my perceptions and feelsings are sound.	1	2	3	4

PERSONAL CHECKLIST

Now, total your scores in each of the health dimensions and compare it to the ideal score. Which areas do you need to work on? How does your score compare with how you rated yourself in the first part of the questionnaire?

Physical Health	40	_____
Social Health	40	_____
Emotional Health	40	_____
Environmental Health	40	_____
Spiritual Health	40	_____
Intellectual Health	40	_____

WHAT YOUR SCORES MEAN

Scores of 35–40: Outstanding! Your answers show that you are aware of the importance of this area to your health. More important, you are putting your knowledge to work for you by practicing good health habits. As long as you continue to do so, this area should not pose a serious health risk. It's likely that you are setting an example for your family and friends to follow. Although you received a very high score on this part of the test, you may want to consider areas where your scores could be improved.

Scores of 30–35: Your health practices in this area are good, but there is room for improvement. Look again at the items you answered that scored one or two points. What changes could you make to improve your score? Even a small change in behavior can often help you achieve better health.

Scores of 20–30: Your health risks are showing! Find information about the risks you are facing and why it is important to change these behaviors. Perhaps you need help in deciding how to make the changes you desire. Assistance is available from your professors, and from student health services at your school.

Scores below 20: You may be taking serious and unnecessary risks with your health. Perhaps you are not aware of the risks and what to do about them. In this lesson and other lessons, you will find information you need to improve your scores and your health.

Source: Donatelle, Rebecca J. *Access to Health* (7th ed.). San Francisco: Benjamin Cummings. 2002. (ISBN: 0-205-33664-7). "How Healthy Are You", pages 6 through 8. (Adapted from *Health Style: A Self-Test,* by U.S. Health and Human Services, 1981, Washington, DC: Public Health Service.)

Physical Fitness and Wellness

The lesson is intended to accomplish the following: 1) raise your awareness of importance of health and wellness; 2) assess personal health and wellness status and discuss methods for improvement; and, 3) assess current stress level and techniques to manage stress.

The following topics are addressed in this lesson:

- Principles and Practices of Wellness

The following TLO is supported in whole or in part by this lesson:

- Implement a Total Fitness Program

Following this lesson you will be able to:

- Identify the elements of a balanced, healthy lifestyle
- Use assessment tools to determine fitness status
- Set personal health goals
- Analyze personal stress levels in terms of principles of wellness

CADET CHECKLIST

____ Go to Blackboard course site for MSL301-Lesson 02 and preview the lesson.

____ Complete the required readings and exercises:

____ 1. Read *Putting Health in Perspective* in the textbook.

____ 2. Read *Improving Your Health* in the textbook.

____ 3. Read *Defining Psychosocial Health* in the textbook.

____ 4. Read *Enhancing Psychosocial Health* in the textbook.

____ 5. Fill out the *Physical Fitness Log* for a one-day period. Remember to bring this to the next class. The log is located in this workbook

____ 6. Complete the online Health Goals Checklist Survey. Fill out, then print and bring to class. http://www.hooah4health.com/4You/hgoalsadultsurvey.asp.

OPTIONAL

____ 1. Fill out the Fitness Log for a period of a week or more.

____ 2. Read *Sleep: The Great Restorer* in the textbook.

____ 3. Read *Spirituality: An Inner Quest for Well-being* in the textbook.

____ 4. Read *The Mind Body Connection* in the textbook.

____ 5. Read *When Psychosocial Health Deteriorates* in the textbook.

____ 6. Read *Suicide: Giving up on Life* in the textbook.

PHYSICAL FITNESS LOG

Name (Last)	First		MI		Rank	Sex (Circle) M F	Organization		

Week	Date	Phase of Training	Exercise Activity No. 1	Reps, Time, Distance, Etc.	Heart Rate Attained	Exercise Activiyie No. 2	Reps, Time, Distance, Etc.	Heart Rate Attained

INSRUCTIONS: 1. Record each worout by entry of date, phase of training, activiyies performed, and heart rate attained. Also indicate the repetitions, time, or other indication of performance for each activity in the block provided. 2. At the end of each week, extend the last horizontal line to the left to indicate the end of the week, and place the number of the week in the weekly column.

FM 21-20, Appendix C

1	**Exercise Title**	How Stressed Are You?
2	**Exercise Number**	MSL301_L02_01C
3	**Type**	Worksheet
4	**Notes**	
5	**Purpose**	Self-assessment to allow cadets to determine the stressors in their lives and their susceptibility to stress.
6	**Directions**	Each of us reacts differently to life's little challenges. Faced with a long line at the bank, most of us will get heated up for a few seconds before we shrug and move on. But for others—such incidents are an assault on good health. That's why rating your stress requires you both to tally your life's stressors (Part One) and to figure out whether you are particularly susceptible to stress (Part Two).

PART ONE

The Stress in Your Life. How often are the following stressful situations a part of your daily life?

1 = Never   2 = Rarely   3 = Sometimes   4 = Often   5 = All the time

I work long hours.	1	2	3	4	5
There are signs that my job isn't secure.	1	2	3	4	5
Doing a good job goes unnoticed.	1	2	3	4	5
It takes all my energy just to make it through a day.	1	2	3	4	5
There are severe arguments at home.	1	2	3	4	5
A family member is seriously ill.	1	2	3	4	5
I'm having problems with child care.	1	2	3	4	5
I don't have enough time for fun.	1	2	3	4	5
I'm on a diet.	1	2	3	4	5
My family and friends count on me to solve their problems.	1	2	3	4	5
I'm expected to keep up a certain standard of living.	1	2	3	4	5
My neighborhood is crowded or dangerous.	1	2	3	4	5
My home is a mess.	1	2	3	4	5
I can't pay my bills on time.	1	2	3	4	5
I'm not saving money.	1	2	3	4	5

Your Total Score _____   _____ _____ _____ _____ _____

Below 38: You have a *Lower-Stress Life.*
38 and Above: You have a *High-Stress Life.*

PART TWO

Your Stress Susceptibility. Try to imagine how you would react in these hypothetical situations.

You've been waiting 20 minutes for a table in a crowded restaurant, and the host seats a party that arrived after you. You feel your anger rise as your face gets hot and your heart beats faster.

TRUE OR FALSE

Your sister calls out of the blue and starts to tell you how much you mean to her. Uncomfortable, you change the subject without expressing what you feel.

TRUE OR FALSE

You come home to find the kitchen looking like a disaster area and your spouse lounging in front of the TV. You tense up and can't seem to shake your anger.

TRUE OR FALSE

Faced with a public speaking event, you get keyed up and lose sleep for a day or more, worrying about how you'll do.

TRUE OR FALSE

On Thursday your repair shop promises to fix your car in time for a weekend trip. As the hours go by, you become increasingly worried that something will go wrong and your trip will be ruined.

TRUE OR FALSE.

Two or Fewer True: You're a *Cool Reactor*, someone who tends to roll with the punches when a situation is out of your control.

Three or More True: Sorry, you're a *Hot Reactor*, someone who responds to mildly stressful situations with a "fight-or-flight" adrenaline rush that drives up blood pressure and can lead to heart rhythm disturbances, accelerated clotting, and damaged blood vessel linings. Some hot reactors can seem cool as a cucumber on the outside, but inside their bodies are silently killing them.

WHAT YOUR SCORES MEAN

Combine the results from Parts One and Two to get your total stress rating.

Lower-Stress Life   Cool Reactor

Whatever your problems, stress isn't one of them. Even when stressful events do occur—and they will—your health probably won't suffer.

Lower-Stress Life   Hot Reactor

You're not under stress—at least for now. Though you tend to overreact to problems, you've wisely managed your life to avoid the big stressors. Before you honk at the guy who cuts you off in rush hour traffic, remember that getting angry can destroy thousands of heart muscle cells within minutes. Robert S. Eliot, author of From Stress to Strength, says hot reactors have no choice but to calm themselves down with rational thought. Ponder the fact that the only thing you'll hasten by reacting is a decline in health. "You have to stop trying to change the world," Eliot advises, "and learn to change your response to it."

High-Stress Life   Cool Reactor

You're under stress, but only you know if it's hurting. Even if you normally thrive with a full plate of challenges, now you might be biting off more than you can chew. Note any increase in headaches, backaches, or insomnia; that's your body telling you to lighten your load. If your job is the main source of stress, think about reducing your hours. If that's not possible, find a way to make your job more enjoyable, and stress will become manageable.

High-Stress Life   Hot Reactor

You're in the danger zone. Make an extra effort to exercise, get enough sleep, and keep your family and friends close. Unfortunately, even being physically fit does little to protect you if your body is in perpetual stress mode. To survive, you may need to make major changes—walking away from a life-destroying job or relationship, perhaps—as well as to develop a whole new approach to life's hourly obstacles. Such effort will be rewarded, too. In one experiment, 77 percent of hot reactors were able to cool down—lower their blood pressure and cholesterol levels—by training themselves to stay calm.

Source: Time Inc. Health from "How Stressed Are You?" Health, October 1994, p. 47. Researched by Lora Elise Ma. (Reprinted by permission of Time Inc. Health in Donatelle, Rebecca J., *Access to Health* (7th ed.) San Francisco: Benjamin Cummings. 2002. (ISBN: 0-205-33664-7). "How Stressed Are You", pages 70 through 71.)

Physical Fitness and Nutrition

This final Physical Well-being lesson examines the influence of diet and lifestyle on total fitness. The lesson is intended to accomplish the following: 1) raise your awareness of the nutrition as it relates to health and physical fitness and wellness; 2) assess personal eating habits for their nutritional value; 3) assess personal attitudes towards nutrition and weight management; and, 4) discuss nutritional foods and the importance of fluid intake.

The following topics are addressed in this lesson:

- Nutrition
- Incorporating healthy eating into everyday life

The following TLO is supported in whole or in part by this lesson:

- Implement a Total Fitness Program

Following this lesson you will be able to:

- Describe elements of nutrition and a healthy diet
- Explain the food pyramid and how to make proper food choices
- Design a personal nutritional program

CADET CHECKLIST

___ Go to Blackboard course site for MSL301-Lesson 03 and preview the lesson.

___ Complete the required readings and exercises:

    ___ 1. Read *Nutrition Basics* in the textbook.

    ___ 2. Review the nutrition section on the Hooah4health.com website. Then try the Food Pyramid Game online at: *http://www.hooah4health.com/body/pyramidinteractive.htm*

    ___ 3. Complete the *Food Habits Log* for a one-day period and bring to class.

OPTIONAL

    ___ 1. Fill out the Fitness Log for a period of a week or more.

    ___ 2. Following class, or at the end of class if time allows, complete either the Reflection Feedback or Summary Review form.

    ___ 3. Following class, or at the end of class if time allows, complete the Cadet Evaluation of Instructor form. As you respond, consider all of the lessons and related experiences that made up this Physical Well-being module.

1	**Exercise Title**	Food Habits Log
2	**Exercise Number**	MSL301_L03_01A
3	**Type**	Log
4	**Notes**	
5	**Purpose**	This is a basic tool that has been adapted to help you record observations you make of food you consume and to become more aware of your nutritional intake.

6	**Directions**

In the spaces provided below, record notes on the food you consume within a one-day period. Print or type clearly. If you require more space, use the back of this worksheet.

Sample:

Time of Day   *8:35 am*

Type of food   *blueberry muffin*

Quantity   *1*

Where did you eat   *In the car, while driving to class*

Why did you eat this particular item? *Hungry and it was quick and inexpensive*

Time of Day

Type of food

Quantity

Where did you eat?

Why did you eat this particular item?

Time of Day

Type of food

Quantity

Where did you eat?

Why did you eat this particular item?

Time of Day

Type of food

Quantity

Where did you eat?

Why did you eat this particular item?

Time of Day

Type of food

Quantity

Where did you eat?

Why did you eat this particular item?

Time of Day

Type of food

Quantity

Where did you eat?

Why did you eat this particular item?

Time of Day

Type of food

Quantity

Where did you eat?

Why did you eat this particular item?

Time of Day

Type of food

Quantity

Where did you eat?

Why did you eat this particular item?

Time of Day

Type of food

Quantity

Where did you eat?

Why did you eat this particular item?

Time of Day

Type of food

Quantity

Where did you eat?

Why did you eat this particular item?

Food Habits Log—One Week

Food Consumed	Day 1		Day 2		Day 3		Day 4		Day 5		Day 6		Day 7	
	Amount Consumed		Amount Consumed		Amount Consumed		Amount Consumed		Amount Consumed		Amount Consumed		Amount Consumed	

1	**Exercise Title**	Your Diet Versus the Food Guide Pyramid
2	**Exercise Number**	MSL301_L03_03C
3	**Type**	Worksheet
4	**Notes**	Source: Insel, Paul M. and Walton T. Roth *Core Concepts In Health* (9th ed.). United States: McGraw Hill, 2001. (ISBN: 0-7674-2370-4). "Nutrition Basics", page 333.
5	**Purpose**	Self-assessment to allow cadets to begin evaluating their daily diet.
6	**Directions**	

1. **Keep a food record:** To evaluate your daily diet, begin by keeping a record of everything you eat on a typical day. To help with your analysis, break down each food item into its component parts and note your serving sizes; for example, a turkey sandwich might be listed as 2 slices sourdough bread, 3 ounces turkey, 1 tomato, 1 tablespoon mayonnaise, and so on.

2. **Compare your servings to the recommendations of the Food Guide Pyramid:** Complete the chart below to compare your daily diet to the Pyramid. See the Table 3.1, in the Cadet Textbook, for the recommended number of servings for your calorie intake. Your portion sizes may have been smaller or larger than the serving sizes given in the Pyramid; translate your intake into actual Pyramid servings as you complete the chart. For example, if you consumed 1 1/2 cups of spaghetti, you would count it as three servings.

Food Group	Pyramid Serving Sizes	Recommended Servings	Actual Servings
Bread, Rice, and Pasta	• 1 slice bread Cereal, • 1 oz ready-to-eat cereal • 1/2 cup cooked cereal, rice, or pasta		
Vegetable	• 1 cup raw leafy vegetables • 1/2 cup other cooked or raw vegetables • 3/4 cup vegetable juice		
Fruit	• 1 medium apple, banana, or orange • 1/2 cup chopped, cooked, or canned fruit • 3/4 cup fruit juice		
Milk, Yogurt, and Cheese	• 1 cup milk or yogurt • 1 1/2 oz natural cheese • 2 oz processed cheese		
Meat, Poultry, Fish, Dry Beans, Eggs, and Nuts	• 2-3 oz cooked lean meat, poultry, or fish • 1 oz meat = 1/2 cup cooked dry beans, 1 egg, 2 tablespoons peanut butter, or 1/3 cup nuts		

Below, list the foods you consumed that don't fit into the major food groups (fats such as mayonnaise, butter, margarine, salad dressing, and sour cream; added sugars such as candy, jam, and regular soda; alcoholic beverages).

3. Evaluate your food choices within the groups: Some choices within each food group are particularly healthy, while others should be eaten only in moderation. To further evaluate your current diet, indicate the number of servings you consumed of the following foods.

Foods to emphasize:

____ whole grains

____ dark-green leafy vegetables

____ orange fruits and vegetables

____ legumes

____ citrus, melon, berries

____ cruciferous vegetables

____ low-fat or nonfat dairy

Food to limit:

____ processed, sweetened grains

____ high-fat meats, poultry skin

____ deep-fried foods

____ full-fat dairy products

____ reg. soda, sweetened teas, fruit drinks

____ foods from the Pyramid tip (fats, sugars)

____ alcoholic beverages

4. Make healthy changes: Bring your diet in line with the Pyramid by adding servings of food groups for which you fall short of the recommendations. To maintain a healthy weight, you may need to balance these additions by reductions in other areas—by eliminating some of the fats, oils, sweets, and alcohol you consume; by cutting extra servings from food groups for which your in-take is more than adequate; or by making healthier choices within the food groups. Make a list of foods to add and a list of foods to eliminate; post your lists in a prominent location.

MODULE II

Personal Development Overview

The Personal Development module is comprised of six lessons divided into two parts: Part I consists of lessons four and five; Part II consists of lessons 13 through 16.

PART I

Lessons four and five are designed to introduce the Leadership Development Program (LDP) that will be used to evaluate your leadership performance and provide you developmental feedback for the rest of your cadet years.

PART II

Lessons 13 through 16 provide you with a set of broadly applicable problem solving concepts, principles, and procedures. A generic model of problem solving is first presented. This problem-solving model is later shown to provide the underlying structure for Army-specific problem solving methods. Consideration of the importance of creative and critical thinking, as well as methods information management are added to the problem solving model to better equip you to engage in a brief problem solving practical exercise at the end of the module.

MODULE II

Personal Development (Part I)

Goal Setting, Feedback, and Introduction to the Leadership Development Program

This class emphasizes the importance of goal setting in producing desirable individual and group outcomes. The importance of the leader's role in goal setting and in providing feedback as the basis for goals is also stressed. The lesson then shifts to Cadet Command's implementation of these principles in the form of the Leadership Development Program.

The following topics are addressed in this lesson:

- Importance of goal setting
- Leader's role in goal setting
- Importance of feedback in goal setting and achievement
- LDP system of feedback and goal setting

The following TLO is supported in whole or in part by this lesson:

- Seek self improvement

Following this lesson you will be able to:

- List the four characteristics of goal setting theory
- Analyze personal goals
- Describe Cadet Command's method of feedback using the Blue Card

CADET CHECKLIST

___Go to Blackboard course site for MSL301-Lesson 04 and preview the lesson.

___Complete the required readings and exercise:

___ 1. Review the Cadet Command Leadership Development Program (LDP) Handbook. This is located on the accompanying CD-ROM. Section 2, paragraph 5, pp. 1–5.

___ 2. Read *Setting Goals* in the textbook.

___ 3. Read *Punishment* in the textbook.

___ 4. Complete the *Charting Your Goals Exercise* in this workbook.

OPTIONAL

___ 1. Following class, or at the end of class if time allows, complete either the Reflection Feedback or Summary Review form.

1	**Exercise Title**	Charting Your Goals Exercise
2	**Exercise Number**	MSL301_L04_01C
3	**Type**	Worksheet
4	**Notes**	
5	**Purpose**	Learn how to set goals and analyze goals, determine what your individual or organizational goals should be, help map out life goals to find a start, and hopefully use the exercise as a stepping-stone to life planning.
6	**Direction**	

1. Brainstorm your individual goals. What do you want to accomplish or become? Do not set limitations—let your mind flow freely.

2. Take about 15 minutes to write down your list.

3. Separate the list into three categories. Are there other categories that work better for you?

   ■ Economic

   ■ Personal development

   ■ Material

4. Label each goal 1, 3, 5 or 10-year goals—what is the timeframe you expect to reach the particular goal.

1	**Exercise Title**	Analysis and Feedback Exercise
2	**Exercise Number**	MSL301_L04_02C
3	**Type**	Worksheet
4	**Notes**	
5	**Purpose**	Learn how to set goals and analyze goals, determine what your individual or organizational goals should be, help map out life goals to find a start and hopefully use the exercise as a stepping-stone to life planning.
6	**Direction**	

Answer the following questions. Consider the goals you have set.

1. Are the goals specific and observable?

2. Are the goals obtainable but challenging?

3. Do these goals require a commitment?

4. Do these goals require feedback?

Leadership Development Program and Self-Assessment

The purpose of this lesson is to ensure you understand the Leadership Development Program (LDP). The sixteen leadership dimensions and the seven Army Values, used to assess your leadership potential within the context of the LDP, will be addressed. The Cadet Evaluation System (CES) will be explained to ensure you are familiar with the evaluation system to include self-assessments.

The following topics are addressed in this lesson:

- 23 assessment dimensions (leadership dimensions & Army Values)
- Operation of Cadet Evaluation System
- Use of Blue & Yellow cards
- Observing, classifying, & rating performance

The following TLOs are supported in whole or in part by this lesson:

- Seek self improvement
- Conduct a self-assessment

Following this lesson you will be able to:

- Describe the Army Leadership Framework—values, attributes, skills, and actions of the "BE, KNOW, and DO" of a leader
- Explain the use of the LDP "blue" and "yellow" cards in relation to cadet self assessment
- Classify performance indicators using the 23 leadership dimensions
- Perform a self-assessment, applying the performance indicators and using the LDP yellow self-assessment card

CADET CHECKLIST

____ Go to Blackboard course site for MSL301-Lessson 05 and preview the lesson.

____ Complete the required readings and exercise:

    ____ 1. Read FM 22-100, Chapter 2. *The Leader and Leadership, What The Leader Must BE, KNOW, and DO.*

    ____ 2. Read FM 22-100 (Appendix B), *Performance Indicators.*

    ____ 3. Complete the Performance Indicators Exercise using information from FM22-100 (Appendix B) *Performance Indicators.*

OPTIONAL

    ____ 1. Following class, or at the end of class if time allows, complete either the Reflection Feedback or Summary Review form.

1	**Exercise Title**	Performance Indicator Exercise
2	**Exercise Number**	MSL301_L05_01C
3	**Type**	Analytic Worksheet
4	**Notes**	
5	**Purpose**	This exercise is designed to test your knowledge and comprehension of the leadership framework and performance indicators used in the Leadership Development Program (LDP).

6	**Direction**
	After studying your homework handout, use Part II of the handout and/or Annex B of FM 22-100, to complete the following assignment.
	In the blank space before each performance indicator, write the mnemonic abbreviation of the leadership dimension below that is best described. Each leadership dimension may be used more than once.

Leadership Doctrine Framework					
Leaders of Character and Competence			Act to achieve excellence by providing Purpose, Direction, and Motivation		
VALUES "BE"	ATTRIBUTES "BE"	SKILLS "KNOW"	ACTIONS "DO"		
			Influencing	Operating	Improving
LO Loyalty	**ME** Mental	**IP** Interpersonal	**CO** Communicating	**PL** Planning	**DE** Developing
DU Duty	**PH** Physical	**CN** Conceptual	**DM** Decision Making	**EX** Executing	**BD** Building
RE Respect	**EM** Emotional	**TE** Technical	**MO** Motivating	**AS** Assessing	**LR** Learning
SS Selfless-Service		**TA** Tactical			
HO Honor					
IT Integrity					
PC Personal Courage					

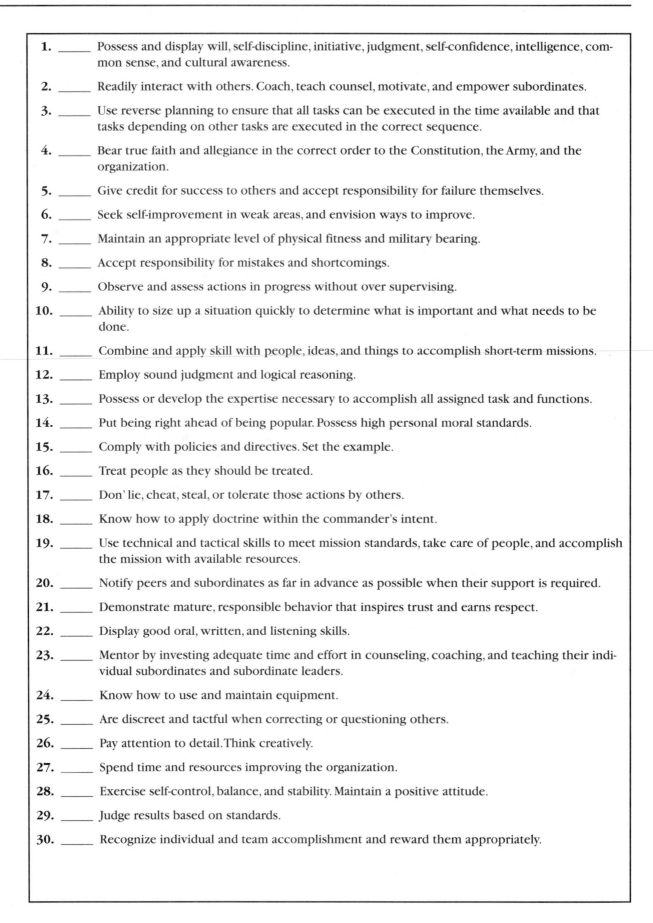

1. _____ Possess and display will, self-discipline, initiative, judgment, self-confidence, intelligence, common sense, and cultural awareness.

2. _____ Readily interact with others. Coach, teach counsel, motivate, and empower subordinates.

3. _____ Use reverse planning to ensure that all tasks can be executed in the time available and that tasks depending on other tasks are executed in the correct sequence.

4. _____ Bear true faith and allegiance in the correct order to the Constitution, the Army, and the organization.

5. _____ Give credit for success to others and accept responsibility for failure themselves.

6. _____ Seek self-improvement in weak areas, and envision ways to improve.

7. _____ Maintain an appropriate level of physical fitness and military bearing.

8. _____ Accept responsibility for mistakes and shortcomings.

9. _____ Observe and assess actions in progress without over supervising.

10. _____ Ability to size up a situation quickly to determine what is important and what needs to be done.

11. _____ Combine and apply skill with people, ideas, and things to accomplish short-term missions.

12. _____ Employ sound judgment and logical reasoning.

13. _____ Possess or develop the expertise necessary to accomplish all assigned task and functions.

14. _____ Put being right ahead of being popular. Possess high personal moral standards.

15. _____ Comply with policies and directives. Set the example.

16. _____ Treat people as they should be treated.

17. _____ Don' lie, cheat, steal, or tolerate those actions by others.

18. _____ Know how to apply doctrine within the commander's intent.

19. _____ Use technical and tactical skills to meet mission standards, take care of people, and accomplish the mission with available resources.

20. _____ Notify peers and subordinates as far in advance as possible when their support is required.

21. _____ Demonstrate mature, responsible behavior that inspires trust and earns respect.

22. _____ Display good oral, written, and listening skills.

23. _____ Mentor by investing adequate time and effort in counseling, coaching, and teaching their individual subordinates and subordinate leaders.

24. _____ Know how to use and maintain equipment.

25. _____ Are discreet and tactful when correcting or questioning others.

26. _____ Pay attention to detail. Think creatively.

27. _____ Spend time and resources improving the organization.

28. _____ Exercise self-control, balance, and stability. Maintain a positive attitude.

29. _____ Judge results based on standards.

30. _____ Recognize individual and team accomplishment and reward them appropriately.

MODULE III

The Army Profession:
Army Operations Overview

This module consists of fifteen lessons divided into two parts: Part I consisting of lessons 6–12; and Part II consisting of lessons 17–24).

PART I

Lesson six and seven are designed to teach you how to plan a block of instruction to be delivered to a small unit. These lessons are intended to prepare you for your responsibilities to prepare and deliver instruction in Military Science and Leadership Labs.

Lessons eight through twelve are designed to introduce you to tactical theory and its battlefield applications. These lessons constitute your classroom introduction to tactics. The principles taught in this module serve as the broad theoretical underpinning to the solution of tactical problems. Historical case studies are used to illustrate tactical principles of offensive and defensive operations and as a capstone exercise for the module. The tactical drills and practice of the MSL Labs complement the theoretical focus of this module.

PART II

Lessons 17 through 24, build on the preceding Personal Development module (Problem Solving lessons 13–16) by examining the Army's adaptation of general problem solving and decision making principles to military operational problems and decisions. The lessons of this module take you through the eight steps of the troop leading procedure including mission analysis, planning, and execution. Sample missions are used throughout this module to give you practical experience in conducting the eight troop leading steps.

MODULE III

The Army Profession:
Army Operations
(Part I)

Train a Team I

This is the first of two lessons on Training a Team, and it is the first lesson in the Army Operations track. As such, it lays the foundation for your success in a key aspect of leadership—training. The lesson is intended to do the following: 1) familiarize you with learning styles, multiple intelligences and information about how you can use soldiers' learning styles to provide more effective training; 2) provide you with information about the Army Training Management System and how leaderships' responsibilities for training and the principles of Army training form the framework for that system; and 3) teach you how to use the Army's crawl-walk-run training process to plan, implement, and assess a training session, including determining whether retraining is a requirement and how it should be conducted.

The following topics are addressed in this lesson:

- Plan training addressing soldiers' learning styles and multiple intelligences
- Establish pre-execution checklists
- Conduct resource coordination
- Train a task
- Assess training
- Conduct retraining

The following TLO is supported in whole or in part by this lesson:

- Apply the Army Training Management System

Following this lesson you will be able to:

- Describe the Army Training Management System
- Plan a training session
- Identify assessment strategies for training

CADET CHECKLIST

___ Go to Blackboard course site for MSL301-Lesson 06 and preview the lesson.

___ Complete the required reading and exercise:

    ___ 1. Take the Learning Style Inventory. (http://www.metamath.com//multiple/multiple_choice_ questions.cgi). Be prepared to discuss how to integrate soldiers' learning styles into the presentation of effective training.

    ___ 2. Read FM 25–101 *Battle Focused Training,* Chapter 1.

    ___ 3. Read "Discovering Your Learning Styles" in the cadet text.

OPTIONAL

    ___ 1. Following class, or at the end of class if time allows, complete either the Reflection Feedback or Summary Review form.

Train a Team II

This is the second of two lessons on Training a Team. Together, the pair lay the foundation for your success in a key aspect of leadership—training. Where the first lesson laid out the principles and practices of effective training, this lesson focuses on practice time with guidance and mentoring from the instructor, and feedback from other cadets.

The following topics are applied in this lesson:

- Reinforcement of leaders' responsibilities for Army training
- The framework of the Army Training Management System
- Feedback in preparing, conducting, and assessing training

The following TLO is supported in whole or in part by this lesson:

- Apply the Army Training Management System

Following this lesson you will be able to:

- Train others in a task, based on a training plan
- Select an assessment strategy
- Assess the training session's effectiveness
- Describe needed retraining
- Implement retraining

CADET CHECKLIST

____ Go to Blackboard course site for MSL301-Lesson 07 and preview the lesson.

____ Prepare for the training:

____ 1. Form a team to do the training (Your instructor may assign members to a team)

____ 2. Select a task from STP 21-1-SMCT, *Soldier's Manual of Common Tasks.* You need to be able to train the task easily during a seven-minute class demonstration.

____ 3. Inform the instructor about the task you selected. Obtain feedback from the instructor as to the task's suitability. You need to do this prior to the class.

____ 4. Create a checklist of what you need. Consult your instructor for assistance on this.

____ 5. Based on the reading lay out how you intend to conduct the training. Do you intend to use flip charts, a computer, posters, and so on? Be sure the classroom can be set up to support your training.

____ 6. Prepare a checklist to assess task performance.

____ 7. Provide a copy of the checklist to your instructor prior to class. Again, obtain feedback.

____ 8. If you have handouts, be sure you have enough copies ready for all members of the class to review.

____ 9. Once you lay out your training strategy, rehearse the roles and task training demonstration at least once.

____ 10. Remember to coordinate materials/equipment requirements with instructor prior to class, especially if you require the instructor's assistance.

OPTIONAL

____ 1. Following class, or at the end of class if time allows, complete either the Reflection Feedback or Summary Review form.

Introduction to Tactics

This is the first in a series of five lessons that provide the framework for tactical principles. This lesson introduces you to basic definitions and concepts of tactics.

The following topics are addressed in this lesson:

- Definition of tactics as both an art and a science
- Relationship and differentiation of the tactical, operational, and strategic levels of warfare
- Definition and description of the battlefield framework and organization
- Battlefield Operating Systems

The following TLO is supported in whole or in part by this lesson:

- Apply tactical principles and doctrine to the solution of tactical problems

Following this lesson you will be able to:

- Define the term tactics
- Describe the differences between the art and science of tactics
- Differentiate among the levels of war
- Describe the basic battlefield framework and organization
- Identify the characteristics of deep, close, and rear operations
- List the Battlefield Operating Systems

CADET CHECKLIST

___ Go to Blackboard course site for MSL301-Lesson 08 and preview the lesson.

___ Complete the required readings and exercise:

    ___ 1. Complete the pre-class Quiz.

    ___ 2. Read FM 3-90 *Tactics*—Chapter 1, paragraphs 1-1 through 1-7, *The Tactical Level of War and The Science and Art of Tactics.*

    ___ 3. Read FM 3-90 *Tactics*—Chapter 2, paragraphs 2-1 through 2-8, *METT-TC and BOS.*

    ___ 4. Read FM 3-0 *Operations*—Chapter 2, paragraphs 2-2 through 2-7, *Levels of War.*

    ___ 5. Read *Fright Night: Task Force 2-34 Armor* in the cadet text.

OPTIONAL

    ___ 1. Following class, or at the end of class if time allows, complete either the Reflection Feedback or Summary Review form.

1	**Exercise Title**	Tactics quiz I
2	**Exercise Number**	MSL301_L08Q
3	**Type**	Quiz
4	**Notes**	
5	**Purpose**	This quiz is the first in a series on tactics to ensure the cadet can define tactics, describe the differences between the art and science of war, differentiate between levels of war, describe the basic battlefield framework and organization, and list the Battlefield Operating Systems (BOS).

| 6 | **Direction** |

After studying your required readings, use Part II of the handout to complete the following assignment.

This is a multiple-choice quiz. In the blank space of each question in the quiz, write the letter that corresponds to the answer that most closely fits the phrase and completes the statement.

TACTICS PRE-CLASS QUIZ

1. _____ is the employment of units in combat. It includes the ordered arrangement and maneuver of units in relation to each other, the terrain and the enemy to translate potential combat power into victorious battles and engagement.
   a. Tactics
   b. Maneuver
   c. Science of war

2. ____ encompasses the understanding of those military aspects of tactics—capabilities, techniques, and procedures—that can be measured and codified.
   a. The art of tactics
   b. The science of tactics
   c. Level of tactics

3. _____ consists of three interrelated aspects: the creative and flexible array of means to accomplish assigned missions, decision making under conditions of uncertainty when faced with an intelligent enemy, and understanding the human dimension—the effects of combat on soldiers.
   a. The art of tactics
   b. The science of tactics
   c. Level of tactics

4. _____ doctrinal perspectives that clarify the links between strategic objectives and tactical actions.
   a. Tactics
   b. Strategy
   c. Levels of war

5. _____ is the lowest level of warfare.
   a. Tactical
   b. Strategic
   c. Operational

6. _____ is the area of operations and battlefield.
   a. Tactics
   b. Maneuver
   c. Battlefield framework

7. Deep, close, and rear operations make up the _____.
   a. Battlefield framework
   b. Battlefield organization
   c. Framework of organization

8. BOS consists of ____ major functions.
   a. Six
   b. Seven
   c. Eight

9. ____ operations preserve the freedom of maneuver of friendly forces.
   a. Intelligence
   b. Mobility
   c. Survivability

10. ____ incorporates a variety of technical specialties and functional activities to maximize the use of logistic support.
    a. Combat Service Support
    b. Command
    c. Control

Army Principles of War

This is the second in a series of five lessons that provide the framework for tactical principles. The first lesson introduced you to basic definitions and concepts, whereas this lesson focuses on types of military operations (offense, defense, stability, and support).

The following topics are addressed in this lesson:

- Principles of war
- Types of tactical operations—offense, defense, stability, and support
- Security and reconnaissance in support of offensive and defensive operations
- Force protection

The following TLO is supported in whole or in part by this lesson:

- Apply tactical principles and doctrine to the solution of tactical problems

Following this lesson you will be able to:

- List the four basic types of military operations
- Define stability operations
- Summarize the army's role in stability operations
- List the nine principles of war and define each
- Define support operations
- Summarize the Army's role in support operations

CADET CHECKLIST

___ Go to Blackboard course site for MSL301-Lesson 09 and preview the lesson.

___ Complete the required readings and exercise:

    ___ 1. Complete the Tactics Pre-Class Quiz 2.

    ___ 2. Read FM 3-0 *Operations*—Pages 4-12 through 4-16, and 9-1 through 9-3, and 10-1 through 10-5.

    ___ 3. Read FM 3-90 *Tactics*—Chapter 2, Chapter 4 pages 4-1 through 4-2, and Chapter 9 pages 9-1 through 9-3.

    ___ 4. Read *Full Circle: World War II to the Persian Gulf* in the cadet text.

OPTIONAL

    ___ 1. Following class, or at the end of class if time allows, complete either the Reflection Feedback or Summary Review form.

1	**Exercise Title**	Tactics Quiz II
2	**Exercise Number**	MSL301_L09Q
3	**Type**	Quiz
4	**Notes**	
5	**Purpose**	This quiz is the second in a series on tactics to ensure the cadet can use the principles of war as a tool in the analysis of plans and operations. The cadet should be able to define each of four types of military operations and summarize the use of stability and support operations.

6	**Direction**

After studying your required readings, use Part II of the handout to complete the following assignment.

This is a multiple-choice quiz. In the blank space of each question in the quiz, write the letter that corresponds to the answer that most closely fits the phrase and completes the statement.

TACTICS PRE-CLASS QUIZ 2

1. ____ a clear understanding of the expected outcome and its impact.
   a. Objective
   b. Offensive
   c. Maneuver

2. ____ the means by which commanders impose their will on an enemy, adversary, or situation.
   a. Objective
   b. Offensive
   c. Maneuver

3. ____ concentrating the effects of combat power against a combination of physical points.
   a. Mass
   b. Offensive
   c. Objective

4. ____ often requires forces to conduct operations with minimum resources.
   a. Unity of Command
   b. Mass
   c. Economy of Force

5. ____ concentrates and disperses military power to place and keep the enemy at a disadvantage.
   a. Maneuver
   b. Mass
   c. Unity of Command

6. ____ means that a single commander directs and coordinates the actions of all forces toward a common objective.
   a. Mass
   b. Economy of Force
   c. Unity of Command

7. ____ results from measures taken by a command to protect itself from surprise, observation, detection, interference, espionage, sabotage, or annoyance.
   a. Surprise
   b. Security
   c. Unity of Command

8. ____ results from taking actions for which an opponent is unprepared.
   a. Security
   b. Surprise
   c. Unity of Command

9. ____ keeps orders understandable, clear, and concise.
   a. Intelligence
   b. Mobility
   c. Simplicity

10. ____ operations aim at destroying or defeating an enemy.
    a. Offensive
    b. Defensive
    c. Stability

Offensive Operations

This is the third in a series of five lessons that provide the framework for tactical principles. The first two lessons introduced you to basic definitions and concepts. At the conclusion of this lesson you will be expected to understand the purposes of offensive operations, the forms of maneuver, and types of offensive operations. Analysis of a case study exposes you to an example of the US Army's offensive role in a recent actual combat operation.

The following topics are addressed in this lesson:

- Purposes of the offense
- Forms of offensive maneuver
- Types of offensive operations
- Offensive operations in Desert Storm

The following TLO is supported in whole or in part by this lesson:

- Apply tactical principles and doctrine to the solution of tactical problems.

Following this lesson you will be able to:

- List and define the characteristics of offensive operations
- Analyze an offensive situation
- Compare and contrast forms of maneuver
- Compare and contrast types of offensive operations

CADET CHECKLIST

___ Go to Blackboard course site for MSL301-Lesson 10 and preview the lesson.

___ Complete the required readings and exercise:

    ___ 1. Complete the Offensive Operations pre-class Quiz.

    ___ 2. Read FM 3-0 Operations, June 2001. Chapter 7, pages 7-1 through 7-7 and 7-11 through 7-27.

OPTIONAL

    ___ 1. Scan FM 3-90 Tactics, July 2001, Part 2: Offensive Operations (Chapters 3 through 7).

    ___ 2. Following class, or at the end of class if time allows, complete either the Reflection Feedback or Summary Review form.

1	**Exercise Title**	Offensive Operations Pre-Class Quiz
2	**Exercise Number**	MSL301_L10Q
3	**Type**	Quiz
4	**Notes**	
5	**Purpose**	This quiz is intended to help the cadet to analyze an operation using the principles of war, and then apply what was learned about systems, principles of war, offense and the forms of maneuver.

6 | **Direction**

After studying your required readings, use Part II of the handout to complete the following assignment.

This is a multiple-choice quiz. In the blank space of each question in the quiz, write the letter that corresponds to the answer that most closely fits the phrase and completes the statement.

OFFENSIVE OPERATIONS PRE-CLASS QUIZ

1. _____ is the characteristic of offensive operations that includes attacking the enemy at a time, place or in a manner for which he is unprepared and for which he did not expect.
   a. Surprise
   b. Concentration
   c. Tempo

2. _____ is the massing of overwhelming effects to achieve a single purpose.
   a. Tempo
   b. Concentration
   c. Audacity

3. _____ is the rate of military action.
   a. Tempo
   b. Concentration
   c. Audacity

4. _____ is a simple plan of action, boldly executed.
   a. Tempo
   b. Surprise
   c. Audacity

5. _____ is a form of maneuver in which an attacking force seeks to avoid the enemy's defenses, by seizing objectives to the enemy's rear to destroy the enemy in their current positions.
   a. Envelopment
   b. Turning movement
   c. Infiltration

6. _____ a form of maneuver in which the attacking force seeks to avoid the enemy's principle defensive positions by seizing objectives to the enemy's rear to cause the enemy to move out of its current positions or divert major forces to meet the threat.
   a. Mass
   b. Envelopment
   c. Turning movement

7. _____ a form of maneuver in which an attacking force conducts undetected movement through or into an area occupied by enemy forces to occupy a position of advantage in the enemy's rear while exposing only small elements to enemy defensive fires.
   a. Envelopment
   b. Infiltration
   c. Turning movement

8. _____ a form of maneuver in which an attacking force seeks to rupture an enemy's defenses on a narrow front to disrupt the defensive system.
   a. Movement to contact
   b. Penetration
   c. Frontal attack

9. _____ a form of maneuver in which an attacking force seeks to destroy a weak enemy force or fix a larger enemy force in place over a broad front.
   a. Movement to contact
   b. Penetration
   c. Frontal attack

10. _____ a type of offensive operation designed to develop the situation and establish or regain contact.
    a. Movement to contact
    b. Attack
    c. Pursuit

1	**Exercise Title**	Operations Analysis Worksheet
2	**Exercise Number**	MSL301_L10_03C
3	**Type**	Worksheet
4	**Notes**	An Operations Analysis Worksheet provides for recording discussion of a learning event. It enables cadets to discover for themselves the relevant details of a video or written case study, and to identify alternative courses of action.
5	**Purpose**	Analyze an operation using the principles of war and apply learning about the art and science of tactics, BOS, principles of war, offense, defense, and the forms of maneuver.
6	**Directions**	

1. Watch the CNN Schwarzkopf Command Briefing video. Observe the offensive operations from the point of view of the commander and prepare to analyze the operation. Apply what you have learned about the art and science of tactics, principles of war, BOS, offense, and the forms of maneuver.

    Identify the key points made by Schwarzkopf in his briefing.

2. Analyze the battle presented in CNN Schwarzkopf Command Briefing.

    What is the overall strategy?

    From the briefing what can you identify in terms of tactics, forms of maneuver, or other offensive operations?

3. Identify contextual (historical, political, economic) factors that limit the situation.

Other Notes

Prepare to report your findings to the class.

Defensive Operations

This is the fourth in a series of five lessons that provide the framework for tactical principles. This lesson focuses on defensive operations—their purposes, characteristics, and the various types of defensive operations. Like the previous lesson, this lesson also provides an example of the US Army's defensive role in an actual historical combat operation where the defense was instrumental in turning the tide of battle.

The following topics are addressed in this lesson:

- Purposes of the defense
- Types of defensive operations
- Defensive operations in the Pusan Perimeter

The following TLO is supported in whole or in part by this lesson:

- Apply tactical principles and doctrine to the solution of tactical problems

Following this lesson you will be able to:

- Identify the characteristics of defensive operations
- Analyze a defensive situation
- List and define types of defensive operations
- Define the terms decisive, shaping and sustaining as they relate to defensive operations

CADET CHECKLIST

____ Go to Blackboard course site for MSL301-Lesson 11 and preview the lesson.

____ Complete the required readings and exercise:

    ____ 1. Complete the Defensive Operations pre-class Quiz.

    ____ 2. Read *The Korean War-The Outbreak* on the cadet CD/text.

    ____ 3. Read FM 3-0 *Operations,* JUNE 2001, paragraphs 8-1 through 8-14 and 8-19 through 8-23.

OPTIONAL

    ____ 1. Following class, or at the end of class if time allows, complete either the Reflection Feedback or Summary Review form.

1	**Exercise Title**	Defensive Operations Pre-Class Quiz
2	**Exercise Number**	MSL301_L11Q
3	**Type**	Pre-Class Quiz
4	**Notes**	
5	**Purpose**	This quiz is intended to help the cadet to analyze a defensive operation using the principles of war, and then apply what they have learned about systems, principles of war, and defensive operations.

6   Direction

After studying your required readings, use Part II of the handout to complete the following assignment.

This is a multiple-choice quiz. In the blank space of each question in the quiz, write the letter that corresponds to the answer that most closely fits the phrase and completes the statement.

DEFENSIVE OPERATIONS PRE-CLASS QUIZ

1. ___ Commanders defend to buy time, hold terrain, facilitate other operations, preoccupy the enemy, or erode enemy resources. They seek out the attacking enemy to strike and weaken him before close combat begins.
   a. True
   b. False
   c. Neither

2. The defender arrives in the Area of Operations (AO) before the attacker and uses the available time for _____. The defender studies the ground and selects defensive positions that mass fires into likely approaches.
   a. Security
   b. Preparation
   c. Measuring effects

3. ___ helps deceive the enemy as to friendly locations, strengths, and weaknesses. These measures provide early warning and disrupt the enemy attack early and continuously.
   a. Security
   b. Disruption
   c. Flexibility

4. ___ stem(s) from well-trained units and clear understanding of the commander's intent.
   a. Disruptions
   b. Mass effects
   c. Flexibility

5. The ____ is a type of defensive operation that concentrates on the destruction or defeat of the enemy through a decisive attack by a striking force.
   a. Mobile defense
   b. Area defense
   c. Retrograde

6. A ____ is a type of defensive operation that involves organized movement away from the enemy.
   a. Mobile Defense
   b. Area Defense
   c. Retrograde

7. A ____ is a form of retrograde that is a planned operation in which a force in contact disengages from an enemy force.
   a. Delay
   b. Withdrawal
   c. Retirement

8. Defeating the enemy attack within an engagement area is the ____ operation.
   a. Shaping
   b. Decisive
   c. Sustaining

9. ___ operations include counter mobility, mobility, reconnaissance, and security operations.
   a. Sustaining
   b. Decisive
   c. Shaping

10. ___ operations occur throughout the area of operations to ensure freedom of action and continuity of the defense.
    a. Sustaining
    b. Decisive
    c. Shaping

1	**Exercise Title**	The Defense of the Pusan Perimeter
2	**Exercise Number**	MSL301_L11_03C
3	**Type**	Case Study Analysis Worksheet
4	**Notes**	A Case Study Analysis Worksheet provides for structured recording of analytic and evaluative notes. Cadets discover for themselves the relevant details of a written case study, and draw conclusions.
5	**Purpose**	Analyze a defensive operation using the principles of war, and apply learning about the art and science of tactics, BOS, principles of war, offense, defense, and the forms of maneuver.
6	**Directions**	

1. Review the in *The Korean War—The Outbreak* reading from the Cadet CD. Apply what you have learned about the art and science of tactics, principles of war, BOS, offense, and the forms of maneuver.

2. Analyze the defensive operation presented in *The Korean War—The Outbreak* with your small group.

    Identify the key points and events.

    What is the overall strategy?

Identify all pertinent references to BOS, defensive operations, and forms of maneuver.

Identify contextual (historical, political, economic) factors that limit the situation.

Other Notes

Prepare to report your findings to the class.

Tactical Analysis Case Study

This is the last in a series of five lessons that provide the framework for tactical principles. This lesson is intended to build the four previous lessons in tactics and to get you to analyze an operation using the principles of war. The analysis of a case study will enable you to pull together, review, reinforce, and apply definitions, concepts, and characteristics of tactical operations to one famous engagement during the Gettysburg Campaign—the Battle for Little Round Top.

The following TLO is supported in whole or in part by this lesson:

- Apply tactical principles and doctrine to the solution of tactical problems

Following this lesson you will be able to:

- Determine the level of war impacted by an operation
- Analyze an operation using the principles of war
- Determine which characteristics of the offense or defense are present during an operation
- Distinguish between the forms of maneuver on the offense and types of operations on the defense

CADET CHECKLIST

___ Go to Blackboard course site for MSL301-Lesson 12 and preview the lesson.

___ Complete the required readings and exercise:

    ___ 1. Read the article *Mantled in Fire and Smoke* in the cadet text.

    ___ 2. Read *The Attack and Defense of Little Round Top* in the cadet text.

    ___ 3. Review the map *Chamberlain at Gettysburg July 2, 1863* in the cadet text.

    ___ 4. Complete the Question Answer Sheet based on the readings. Respond with brief but clear statements.

OPTIONAL

    ___ 1. Read FM 3-90 *Tactics.* Part 2, Offensive Operations (Chapters 3 through 7) on the cadet CD.

    ___ 2. Review Previous readings from FM 3-0 *Operations* and 3-90 *Tactics* on the cadet CD.

    ___ 3. View *Gettysburg* (the movie).

    ___ 4. Following class, or at the end of class if time allows, complete either the Reflection Feedback or Summary Review form.

1	**Exercise Title**	Tactical Analysis
2	**Exercise Number**	MSL301_L12_01C
3	**Type**	Question Answer Sheet
4	**Notes**	
5	**Purpose**	This question answer sheet is intended to reinforce and clarify the cadet's understanding of the readings. The cadet also analyzes the readings based on what was learned regarding the principles of war and operations.

| 6 | **Direction** |

After studying your required readings, review the following questions.

In the blank space beneath each question, give your answer in clear, concise and complete sentences.

1. Which part of tactics—the art or the science—caused victory or defeat in the Battle for Little Round Top (LRT)?

2. What levels of war were involved in the Battle for Little Round Top?

3. Describe, using a short answer of two to three sentences, the application of each of the nine principles of war to your side of the Battle for Little Round Top.

4. Which characteristics of the offense did COL Oates' force use? Justify your answer.

5. Which forms of maneuver did COL Oates use?

6. Why was his attack unsuccessful?

7. Which characteristics of defensive operations did COL Chamberlain use? Justify your answer.

8. Which types of defensive operations did the 20th Maine use?

9. Why was COL Chamberlain's defense successful?

1	**Exercise Title**	Little Round Top Tactical Analysis
2	**Exercise Number**	MSL301_L12_03C
3	**Type**	Case Study Analysis Worksheet
4	**Notes**	A Case Study Analysis Worksheet provides guidance so that the cadet can respond to questions and discussion about an historical event/case study. This approach enables cadets to discover for themselves the relevant details of a video or a written case study, and then to identify alternative courses of action.
5	**Purpose**	Analyze an operation using the principles of war, and apply learning about the art and science of tactics, BOS, principles of war, offense, defense, and the forms of maneuver.

6	**Directions**

1. The instructor divides the class in to groups. The instructor assigns each group a role—either Confederate or Union.

2. The instructor shows a video clip from a famous scene called The Battle of Little Round Top. This is from the movie, Gettysburg.

3. You are to analyze the battle from the point of view of either the Confederate commander or the Union Commander.

Observe the operations from the point of view of the commanders and prepare to analyze the operation.

Apply what you have learned about the art and science of tactics, principles of war, BOS, offense, and the forms of maneuver.

4. You have 10 minutes to analyze the battle presented in the video clip. Record your observations. Prepare to report your findings to the class.

The exercise provides you with an opportunity to use your knowledge of basic tactics. Analyze the engagement. Remember this battle had a major impact on the outcome of not only a campaign, but ultimately the war.

If the Confederates had won this engagement, then the Union Army could easily have LOST THE WAR.

What would have happened to this country if Col Chamberlain had not held his ground?

This battle demonstrates the principles of war, the science and art of tactics, and also offensive and defensive operations. Remember your basic tactics lessons—you will use them not only throughout your ROTC training, but also as a foundation for your education as an officer in the US Army.

NOTES

MODULE II

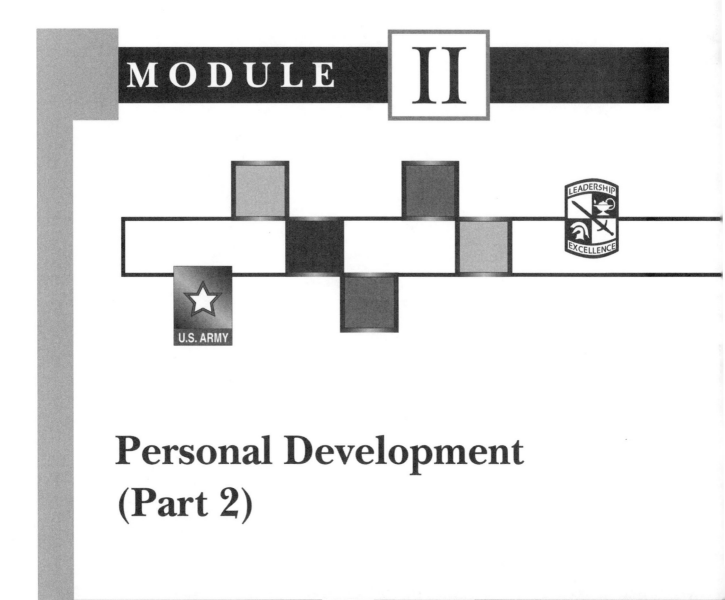

Personal Development
(Part 2)

Part II of the Personal Development module consists of lessons 13 through 16, which focus developing reasoning skills. This series of four lessons provides a foundation for developing leadership skills by providing you with a set of broadly applicable problem solving concepts, principles, and procedures. All four lessons address the seven-step Army problem-solving process described in FM 22-100. The first lesson provides an overview and begins a step-by-step examination of the process. The step-by-step examination continues through the third lesson and allows you to practice the skills of each step. The fourth lesson provides higher-level practice by requiring you to work in teams, and apply the entire process to a moderately complex problem situation. This problem-solving module provides a sound foundation for the problem-solving aspects of the lessons in the Army Operations module that immediately follows.

Problem Solving— Identifying the Problem

The first lesson provides an overview and begins a step-by-step examination of the Army problem solving process. The intent of this lesson is not to make you an expert problem solver, but rather to expose you to a formalized and general process that you can adapt and apply to both military and daily life situations.

The following topics are addressed in this lesson:

- General model of problem solving
- Problem solving heuristics
- Problem statements
- The Army problem solving model

The following TLO is supported in whole or in part by this lesson:

- Solve problems

Following this lesson you will be able to:

- Describe the seven-step Army problem-solving process
- Identify specified, implied, and critical tasks for a given problem or mission
- Develop a problem statement from a situational description

CADET CHECKLIST

___ Go to Blackboard course site for MSL301-Lesson 13 and preview the lesson.

___ Complete the required readings and pre-class activity:

  ___ 1. Complete the "Identify the Problem" worksheet in this workbook. Bring statements to class for discussion and feedback.

  ___ 2. Read *The Army Problem Solving Process* in the textbook.

  ___ 3. Read FM 22-100 *Army Leadership: Be, Know, Do*, Aug 1999, Chapter 5 pages 5-3 through 5-6 *Decision Making* on the cadet CD.

OPTIONAL

  ___ 1. Watch *Apollo 13*.

  ___ 2. Following class, or at the end of class if time allows, complete either the *Reflection Feedback* or *Summary Review* form.

1	**Exercise Title**	Identifying the Problem
2	**Exercise Number**	MSL301_L13_02C
3	**Type**	Worksheet
4	**Notes**	This is a pre-class activity.
5	**Purpose**	Construct problem statements.
6	**Directions**	

Directions

Write a problem statement for each of the problem situations described below. Your problem statement should address the root problem and not confuse symptoms with the problem. In addition, where applicable, identify any tasks that are specified or implied in the problem situation and indicate which tasks are critical to the solution of the problem. Take your written responses to class for review and discussion.

Situation 1: As you drive to work each morning, you are confronted with intensely heavy traffic at the corner of Fourth and Elm. On several occasions, this has caused you to be late for work. Your supervisor is unhappy with you, and you are in danger of losing your job because of your chronic lateness.

Problem Statement:

Situation 2: From the post semi-annual expense accounting, the Post Commander has determined that the cost of power mower maintenance for the first 6 months of the current fiscal year is 40 percent higher than the cost of mower maintenance for the first 6 months of last fiscal year. The Commander has directed you, the Director of Logistics (DOL), to cut the cost of mower maintenance to a level that will ensure this year's total maintenance cost will not exceed last year's total cost.

Problem Statement:

Situation 3: You work as the Assistant Director of the Management Training Branch (MTB) of Mega-Bank, Inc. MTB provides custom training to middle and upper level managers and executives within the five divisions of Mega-Bank. The Management Training Branch functions as an internal enterprise in that it generates its own business by advertising its services and capabilities to the Bank's divisions. Subordinate business units of Mega-Bank award contracts to MTB for the production and delivery of management training to meet the specific needs of the business unit. MTB is responsible for hiring its own personnel, purchasing its own equipment and supplies, paying for travel expenses, and renting training facilities. Over the last two years, the demand for MTB services has grown considerably and there is now a seven-week backlog of training programs to be developed and delivered.

One day, your boss, the Director of MTB, shows you a memorandum just received from the Corporate Vice President for Internal Services and Support. The memorandum suggests that the Management Training Branch is not providing sufficient benefit to Mega-Bank's profitability and that the Board of Directors is considering elimination of MTB. The memorandum's allegation is shocking because demand for MTB services has never been higher and feedback on the benefits of MTB training has been filled with enthusiastic praise.

Problem Statement:

Problem Solving–
Developing Solutions

This lesson continues the step-by-step examination and practice of the seven steps of the Army problem-solving process. The lesson is divided into two main parts. In the first part, you will apply analytic skills to identify needed information, categorize information, and evaluate the validity and utility of information. In the second part, you will apply creative thinking skills to generate potential solutions to a problem situation. In doing this, you will gain practical experience in brainstorming. Impediments to creative thinking are also illustrated as part of pre-class activity assignments.

The following topics are addressed in this lesson:

- Application of the general model of problem solving
- Creative thinking
- Brainstorming methods to identify courses of action
- Use of screening and evaluation criteria

The following TLOs are supported in whole or in part by this lesson:

- Apply critical thinking skills
- Solve problems

Following this lesson you will be able to:

- Classify information as fact, assumption, criterion, opinion, or definition
- Assess the importance and accuracy of information using critical thinking skills
- Apply brainstorming techniques to generate potential problem solutions
- List common impediments to creative thinking

CADET CHECKLIST

___ Go to Blackboard course site for MSL301-Lesson 14 and preview the lesson.

___ Complete the required reading and exercise:

    ___ 1. Review *Solving Problems.*

    ___ 2. Complete the Problem Solving pre-class Quiz.

OPTIONAL

    ___ 1. Following class, or at the end of class if time allows, complete either the *Reflection Feedback* or *Summary Review* form.

PROBLEM SOLVING PRE-CLASS QUIZ

INSTRUCTIONS

Based on the pre-class reading for this lesson, select the best answer for each of the questions below. Indicate your selection by circling it.

1. Backward planning is a variation of which method of generating solutions to problems?
   A. trial and error
   B. means-ends analysis
   C. subgoal development
   D. insight generation

2. A psychologist shows one group of individuals a 30-minute videotape entitled "The Worst Air Disasters of the Twentieth Century." A second group is shown a 30-minute tape entitled "Nutrition for Better Living." After seeing the videotapes, members of both groups are asked to estimate the probability of being involved in an airline crash when traveling by airplane. Members of the first group give probability estimates that are 15 times greater than the estimates given by the second group. This result illustrates:
   A. algorithmic thinking
   B. insight
   C. rational-emotive bias
   D. availability heuristic

3. The primary purpose of brainstorming is:
   A. to produce high quality ideas
   B. to compare courses of action
   C. to generate a large number of ideas
   D. to establish screening and evaluation criteria

4. During a survival exercise, Rupert figured-out how to start a fire with his eye glass lens, make a snare trigger with elastic from his jacket, and create a water filter with charcoal and sand inside a metal can. Rupert's ability to use common objects in creative ways probably indicates that he *did not* suffer from:
   A. operant conditioning
   B. learned helplessness
   C. functional fixedness
   D. fundamental attribution error

5. John grew-up on a farm that employed many poor and illiterate migrant workers from Mexico to harvest crops. Now in college, whenever John meets an Hispanic fellow student, he speaks to the student slowly and uses simple words. This behavior illustrates:
   A. representativeness heuristic
   B. syllogistic reasoning
   C. reflective judgment
   D. intrinsic motivation

6. Early in the season, the coach gave the team members a stern reminder to be on time for team practice sessions. As he said this, he happened to be staring directly at Matt, who had been late to several practices. Matt concluded that the coach had singled him out and had really meant the criticism for him. For the rest of the season, Matt misinterpreted many of the coach's statements as evidence of the coach's continuing disappointment with him. Matt seemed to not notice the frequent praise that the coach gave to Matt. Matt's continuing misinterpretation of the situation is an example of:
   A. confirmation bias
   B. paranoia
   C. fixation effect
   D. deductive reasoning

7. In high school, Felecia would often wait until the night before a paper was due before beginning it. Her superior verbal skills enabled her to earn good grades on her papers by simply padding a few facts, obtained from an encyclopedia, with elaborately worded introductory sentences, opinions, transition sentences, and closing paragraphs. Now in college, she continues to use the same methods despite earning poor grades on her papers. Felecia's continued use of her old methods illustrates:
   A. convergent thinking
   B. social learning
   C. homeostasis
   D. mental set

1	**Exercise Title**	Problem Situation #1
2	**Exercise Number**	MSL301_L14_02C
3	**Type**	Worksheet
4	**Notes**	You have 10 minutes for this exercise.
5	**Purpose**	To enhance cadets' ability to solve problems by introducing problem analysis and brainstorming techniques.
6	**Directions** Read Problem Situation #1. As you do, make notes. Use the Analytic Worksheet for your notetaking.	

PROBLEM SITUATION #1

You are the new production manager for Cybertron, Inc., a company that designs and manufactures custom circuit boards for handheld electronic devices such as cell phones, pagers, and personal digital assistants. Cybertron's circuit boards are sold to major end-product companies around the world. As production manager, you supervise the manufacturing arm of Cybertron. You are responsible for seeing that circuit boards are produced to specification, meet the highest quality standards, cost the least possible, and are ready by the customers' deadlines.

Late last week, when you took over as production manager, your boss, the corporate vice-president for operations, told you of a production problem that Cybertron is experiencing. Over the last three months, key production indicators have slipped. The rate of production has declined 13 percent and the number of defective circuit boards found by the quality control unit has risen 8 percent. During the same time period, employee sick-day absences have risen 17 percent. Additionally, due to production delays, Cybertron has twice been late in delivering circuit boards to one of its biggest customers. Your boss was clearly unhappy with the decline in production performance and implied that the inability of your predecessor to fix the problem was a major factor in the decision to fire him and hire you. You now have the responsibility to solve this vexing problem.

NOTES

Analytic Worksheet

Information	Type of Information	Essential	Notes

1	**Exercise Title**	Problem Situation #2
2	**Exercise Number**	MSL301_L14_03C
3	**Type**	Worksheet
4	**Notes**	You have 14 minutes for this exercise.
5	**Purpose**	To enhance cadets' ability to solve problems by introducing problem analysis and brainstorming techniques.
6	**Directions** Read Problem Situation #2. As you do, make notes. Then, fill in the accompanying analytic worksheet.	

PROBLEM SITUATION #2

As an Army Acquisition Corps officer, you are a member of the Advanced Antitank Missile (AATM) project management team. The mission of the team is to develop the specifications for a new generation fire and forget antitank missile that will be fired from the Army's new Future Fighting Vehicle (FFV) which is also currently in development. To accomplish this mission, you and your fellow members of the AATM team must determine the performance specifications that the AATM must meet, identify candidate missiles from those currently in production or development by NATO armament companies, and communicate Army needs to the candidate companies. As the AATM project management team begins its work, it first reviews the information it has on hand:

Army operations and doctrine developers have specified a need for a fire and forget antitank missile capable of exceeding the range of the Army's current TOW-IIA by one third at no increase in time of flight or decrease in probability of hit (PH). In addition, the new missile must be effective against new generations of enemy hardened and reactive armor. The new missile must be capable of being loaded into the FFV mounted launcher by a single soldier. The AATM is to be this missile.

The Future Fighting Vehicle, which will be the primary platform from which the AATM is fired, is to be a light weight (under 21 tons), air-transportable, wheeled (6 X 6 or 8 X 8), armored fighting vehicle, capable of carrying a crew of three (driver, gunner, and commander) plus an infantry squad of 10 combat equipped soldiers. The FFV will use advanced composite armor to give it excellent protective characteristics while saving weight. The light weight of the FFV, coupled with its turbocharged multi-fuel engine will enable it to travel at road speeds in excess of 50 miles per hour. This powerful engine plus the FFV's 14 inches of wheel travel will also permit off-road speeds of 30 mph or more depending on the actual nature of the terrain. The primary armament is housed in a single-person turret and consists of the AATM launcher, an automatic 40mm grenade launcher, and a 7.62mm machinegun. The FFV will be capable of carrying two AATM missiles pre-loaded in the launcher and has an internal storage rack capable of holding six additional missiles, each up to 8 inches in diameter and 51 inches in length. The FFV will carry up to 250 rounds of 40mm grenade ammunition and 2,000 rounds of 7.62mm machinegun ammunition. To minimize the turret profile, only the commander occupies the turret. The gunner is positioned at a gunner's station located behind the driver.

Four armament companies have or are designing missiles that they intend to submit in competition for the AATM contract, which is estimated to be worth $730M in its first three years. Information on these missiles and the current TOW-IIA is given in the table below:

Characteristic	TOW-IIA (USA)	Luchs K2 (Germany)	Águila 5 (Spain)	Åskskräll (Sweden)	Collins (M4) (Sweden)
Weight (kg)	22.7	31.3	28.4	40.9	33.1
Length (cm)	128	126	125	126	131
Diameter (cm)	15	20	20.2	20	20.1
Maximum velocity (mps)	329	489	453	555	480 est.
Time of flight (sec)	20	22	18	20	
Explosive filler (kg)	3.1	4.5	4.2	5.7	4.9
Warhead type	tandem	FOSD	tandem	tandem	FOSD
Temperature range (°C)	−29/+52	−26/+46	−23/+50	−32/+41	
Slew rate (deg/sec)	15	21	19	22	20
Tracking sensor	gunner	thermal	computed	contrast	thermal
Status	U.S. std.	prototype	in use	in use	in design

FOSD = Fly Over / Shoot Down

NOTES

Analytic Worksheet

Information	Type of Information	Essential	Notes

INFORMATION ANALYSIS WORKSHEET

PURPOSE

This worksheet is designed to help you analyze available information and identify information needs related to the solution of a problem. These activities are part of step two, *Identify Facts and Assumptions,* of the Army problem solving process.

CATEGORIES OF INFORMATION

Information used in the solution of problems can be classified into five categories:

1. **Fact:** Information that you *know* about the situation. An event, past or present, that has been personally observed or has been observed and reported to you is a fact. Documents such as Army manuals, regulations, and policies, as well as references and texts may also provide relevant facts. When using such sources, you must determine whether the publication is providing information that is always true, sometime true, or simply conjecture or opinion.
2. **Assumption:** A statement that you *believe* to be true but do not have facts to verify its truth. When solving problems, assumptions should be kept to a minimum. You should make only those assumptions that are essential to generating solutions to the problem.
3. **Criteria:** The information that defines the limits within which the solution to a problem must fall. Criteria are used to determine which solution is best. There are two types of criteria:
   - **Screening Criteria:** *Essential features* that any acceptable solution to the problem must possess. If a potential course of action fails to meet even a single screening criterion, that course of action is rejected.
   - **Evaluation Criteria:** *Features that we desire* the problem solution to provide, but which are not truly essential. Evaluation criteria and screening criteria often deal with the same aspect of the problem and differ only in degree. For example, if the Army is purchasing a new truck that must be able to carry at least 5 tons of cargo, we would apply the 5-ton limit as a screening criterion and eliminate from our consideration any trucks that cannot carry 5 tons. When examining the remaining trucks, we would consider the load capacity of the trucks as an evaluation criterion and look more favorably on those trucks that can carry more than 5 tons.
   - **Benchmark:** A value that represents the *preferred state of an evaluation criterion.* Benchmarks help us determine if an alternative is good enough or desirable. While not being overly demanding, benchmarks indicate the value or level of performance that we consider to be clearly advantageous or desirable. For example, while a 5-ton capacity may be the minimum acceptable standard for the new truck, we might determine that a 7-ton capacity is desirable (and reasonable) and establish a 7-ton capacity as a benchmark. We would consider trucks with capacities between 5 and 7 tons, but look favorably on trucks with capacities of 7 or more tons.
4. **Opinion:** A personal judgment that you have made or that some other individual has made.
5. **Definition:** Used to clarify technical terms, to provide precise nomenclature on particular equipment, or to describe specific operations or procedures that may not be familiar to you or others involved in the problem-solving situation.

INSTRUCTIONS

Examine the problem situation and list the relevant elements of information that you have. Categorize each element of information as fact, assumption, criterion, opinion, or definition. Finally, indicate the importance or use of each element of information for the solution of the problem. Make sure that all assumptions are essential for reaching a problem solution.

Element of Information	Category	Importance/Use

After analyzing the information that you have on hand, determine what information you still need to solve the problem and the most likely source of that information.

Needed Information	Importance/Use	Likely Source

Problem Solving— Evaluating Solutions

This is the third in a series of four lessons on problem solving. This lesson focuses on the identification and application of screening and evaluation criteria to compare and to select the best problem solution from among alternatives. The intent of this lesson is to enhance your ability to solve problems by introducing the concepts of screening and evaluation criteria and practicing the systematic application of criteria to select the best solution to a problem from among alternatives.

The following topics are addressed in this lesson:

- Screening and evaluation criteria
- Simply decision matrices
- Application of solution alternatives

The following TLOs are supported in whole or in part by this lesson:

- Apply critical thinking skills
- Solve problems

Following this lesson you will be able to:

- Analyze a problem
- Identify screening and evaluation criteria appropriate to problem solving
- Apply simple decision matrices to select the best course of action

CADET CHECKLIST

___ Go to Blackboard course site for MSL301-Lesson 15 and preview the lesson.

___ Complete the required reading and exercise:

    ___ 1. Read *Comparing Alternatives.*

    ___ 2. Complete pre-class activity: *Comparing Alternatives.* Be sure to bring your written results of the exercise to class.

OPTIONAL

    ___ 1. Following class, or at the end of class if time allows, complete either the *Reflection Feedback* or *Summary Review* form.

COMPARING ALTERNATIVES
PRE-CLASS ACTIVITY

INSTRUCTIONS

Complete this pre-class exercise and take your written results to class for review.

SITUATION

As a member of a brigade S3 section you have developed three offensive courses of action. You have war gamed (analyzed) these courses of action and reached the following conclusions:

Main Attack in the East: The main effort will be against the enemy's weakest concentration along an axis of advance of 28 km in length. We expect to encounter a limited number of obstacles. The course of action is very susceptible to enemy control of key terrain which overlooks the axis of advance. We expect a moderate tempo of advance for this course of action.

Main Attack in the Center: The main effort will be mounted against moderate enemy concentrations along an axis of advance of 23 km in length. We expect to encounter a moderate number of obstacles. The course of action provides for control of some key terrain in sector but is subject to enemy control of the remaining key terrain. This course of action provides for the fastest tempo of advance.

Main Attack in the West: The main effort will be mounted against the enemy's strongest concentrations along an axis of advance of 20 km in length. We expect to encounter a large number of obstacles. This course of action provides for control of all key terrain in sector. It becomes the course of action with the slowest tempo of advance.

REQUIREMENT

A. What screening criteria, if any, would you establish for this problem?

B. What evaluation criteria would you establish for this problem?

C. Produce a raw data matrix that shows how each course of action fares on each of the evaluation criteria.

D. Convert your raw data matrix to a +/- decision matrix, assigning equal weights to all evaluation criteria. Which course of action would you recommend?

+/- DECISION MATRIX
CLASSROOM EXERCISE

SITUATION

You and four of your friends have decided to use your spring break to go on a late-season ski trip to Colorado. You have searched the Internet to identify ski resorts with special deals and have found three resorts that look promising. All three resorts are in the same general area. While each has its own ski slopes, their proximity to each other would allow you to easily reach any of the three resorts' slopes. Here are the results of your search:

Ski Fremont—A moderate sized resort with many amenities. Ski Fremont offers two bedroom apartments that can sleep four, although a roll-in cot can be added for an additional fee of $15 per night. Each apartment has a full kitchen and cable TV. The resort has a restaurant (serving only dinner), a cafeteria, coffee shop, night club, and convenience store on the premises. A fully equipped weight room, sauna, hot tub, and indoor swimming pool are also available to guests free of charge. Ski Fremont has 15 ski runs, two of which are reserved for snow-boarders. The ski slope is a 7 minute ride on the shuttle bus which runs every 20 minutes when the slopes are open. Ski Fremont offers a package deal which includes lodging for 4 nights and 5 days, lift tickets for 4 days, and meal vouchers worth $100 in any Ski Fremont eating facility. This package costs $725 per person based on four-person occupancy.

Snow Path Mountain—A very large ski resort featuring a wide range of accommodations and 23 slopes. Snow Path offers a package deal that combines lodging and lift tickets. This deal includes a 3 bedroom townhouse with full kitchen that sleeps six for 4 nights and lift tickets for 4 days. In addition, there is a free welcome party in the main lodge on the night of arrival. The cost of this package is $565 per person based on six-person occupancy. Snow Path also offers the convenience of ski-in ski-out slope access, two restaurants and a coffee shop on the premises, and $5 off of lift tickets at other local resorts.

Winter Glen—A relatively small resort with hotel style rooms that can accommodate two people each. Rooms have no cooking facilities, but they do have a small refrigerator. The lodge is located close to the lift area and features ski-in ski-out convenience to the resort's 8 ski runs. The cost of a 4-night, 5-day stay is $320 based on double occupancy and $400 for single occupancy. Lift tickets are $47 per day or $172 for a 4-day ticket. Several restaurants are within a short drive of the lodge.

REQUIREMENT

A. What screening criteria, if any, would you establish for this problem?

B. What evaluation criteria would you establish for this problem?

C. Produce a raw data matrix that shows how each course of action fares on each of the evaluation criteria.

D. Convert your raw data matrix to a +/- decision matrix. Weight the evaluation criteria as you see fit, but be able to explain your weighting. Which course of action would you recommend?

RELATIVE VALUES DECISION MATRIX
ILLUSTRATION

PURPOSE

This document supports the instructor's demonstration of how to apply steps 4, 5, and 6 of the Army problem solving process when a relative values decision matrix is used to compare alternatives. Cadets will have read about the use of +/- and relative values decision matrices before class, and will have completed two +/- decision matrices, one as a pre-class activity and the second as an in-class activity.

The focus of this illustration is on the identification of screening and evaluation criteria, deciding how to weight evaluation criteria, and the proper construction of a relative values decision matrix.

SITUATION

The cadets of the ROTC battalion's military ball planning committee are trying to decide where to hold the military ball this year. The military ball has traditionally been the highlight of the ROTC social activities for the year. Nearly every cadet attends the military ball and virtually all who attend take a date. In fact, this year 120 cadets paid their military ball deposit by the cutoff date. The goal of the planning committee is to have a fun, safe, and memorable military ball that will not be too expensive for the cadets. The sequence of events for the ball will be: commander's reception line, posting of the colors, toasts, dinner, commander's remarks, retirement of the colors, and dancing. Music for the dancing will be provided by a DJ.

To help defray the costs of the military ball, the 128 cadets of the battalion have participated in a number of fundraising events, including directing parking at football games, providing support to the college's annual 10K road race, and raffling a round-trip airplane ticket for two to Cancun for spring break. These efforts have earned the battalion a total of $3,046.40 for the military ball fund. The planning committee has decided that the total cost of attendance for cadet and date may not exceed $35.

The planning committee is considering three locations for this year's military ball:

Westside Marquis Hotel—This is a modern high-rise hotel located in the western part of a nearby city, approximately 35 miles from campus. There is ample free parking in the hotel's underground garage. The Westside Marquis has several nicely decorated ballrooms of varying sizes, but only the Crown Room is available on the night of the military ball. The Crown Room is capable of seating up to 325 dinner guests and has a wooden dance floor and a bandstand at one end. The Westside Marquis will provide a buffet style dinner, wait staff for drinks and dessert, and DJ for the flat rate of $28.50 per person if a minimum of 200 people attend. The ballroom can be used until 1:00 am.

Fort Taylor Officers Club—Fort Taylor is a Reserve Component post located approximately 18 miles from campus. Although it has a small full-time garrison, Fort Taylor is most active on the weekends and during the summer months, which are the prime times for Reserve Component active duty training. The Fort Taylor Officers Club is normally closed, except for the active summer months and for special occasions scheduled at various times throughout the year. The building is old but functional. The club contains a single ballroom capable of seating a maximum of seating 240 guests if eight-person round tables are used and 260 if ten-person rectangular tables are used. A modest sized dance floor is available in an adjacent room. The Fort Taylor Officers Club will serve meals at the tables. The rental fee for the facilities is a flat $1,200, the meal is $21.00 per person if a minimum of 200 people attend, and the DJ costs $350 for up to three hours of dancing. The ballroom can be used until 12:00 am.

Oak Mountain Country Club—The Oak Mountain Country Club is an elegant establishment located 3 1/2 miles from campus. The club is in high demand for various functions, but is available on the night of the military ball. The manager, who is a former Army food service warrant officer, has agreed to give the ROTC battalion a special break on pricing. He is willing to provide the Laurel Ballroom, a buffet dinner for up to 260, and DJ for the flat rate of $7,200. Although the Laurel Ballroom is not large enough to provide a dance floor when feeding this number of people, the ballroom opens onto a large awning-covered patio that would be large enough to serve as a dance floor. The temperatures at the time of year when the military ball will be held are usually mild enough to make outdoor dancing a reasonable option. The patio offers the added advantage of offering a beautiful view of the nighttime lights in the valley below. The ballroom can be used until 1:00 am.

The planning committee has accomplished the first three steps of the Army problem solving process and must now continue the process to determine where the military ball will be held this year.

Steps Completed

Step 1—Identify the Problem

Where should the military ball be held this year?

Step 2—Identify Facts and Assumptions

- Assume that 120 cadets, each with a date, will attend the military ball.
- The cadet battalion has $3,046.40 that it will use to offset the cost of the military ball.

Step 3—Generate Alternatives

See alternatives listed above.

Steps Remaining

Step 4—Analyze the Alternatives

A. In the space below, list the screening and evaluation criteria that you will use in solving this problem.

B. Examine each alternative solution to identify its intended and unintended consequences, resource or other constraints, and advantages and disadvantages. Also analyze each alternative solution in terms of the screening and evaluation criteria you listed above.

- *Westside Marquis Hotel:*

■ *Fort Taylor Officers Club:*

■ *Oak Mountain Country Club:*

Step 5—Compare the Alternatives

A. Apply the screening criteria to eliminate any alternatives that do not meet the one or more screening criteria. List any alternatives that are eliminated.

B. Use the empty matrix below to construct a raw data matrix to compare the surviving alternatives on the evaluation criteria. Include the weights that you will assign to each evaluation criterion, if you choose to weight them. Note: You may need to alter the dimensions of the matrix to accommodate the number of alternatives and evaluation criteria that you identify.

Military Ball Location						
Name →						
Criterion Weight →						

Step 6—Make and Execute Your Decision

Use the empty matrix below to convert the raw data matrix you just completed into a relative values matrix. For each alternative, give both the unweighted and weighted relative value for each of the evaluation criteria.

Add the weighted relative values for each alternative and enter the total in the right-most column. Circle the alternative total that has the lowest value to indicate the best decision.

Military Ball Location							
Name →							**Total** ↓
Criterion Weight →							

Problem Solving— Practical Exercise

This is the last in the series of four lessons on problem solving. This lesson provides you with the opportunity to apply what has been learned in previous lessons and to practice several aspects of problem solving. This lesson fosters practice in the application of the Army problem-solving process to a moderately complex real-world situation.

The following topics are addressed in this lesson:

- Application of the Army problem solving model
- Use of time and information management techniques
- Development and use of screening and evaluation criteria
- Application of creative and critical thinking

The following TLOs are supported in whole or in part by this lesson:

- Apply critical thinking skills
- Solve problems

Following this lesson you will be able to:

- Apply the seven-step Army problem solving process
- Communicate the seven step problem-solving process to peers

CADET CHECKLIST

___ Go to Blackboard course site for MSL301-Lesson 16 and preview the lesson.

___ Complete the required readings:

    ___ 1. Review *The Army Problem Solving Process* located in Lesson 13.

    ___ 2. Review *Comparing Alternatives* located in lesson 15.

OPTIONAL

    ___ 1. Following class, or at the end of class if time allows, complete either the Reflection Feedback or Summary Review form.

    ___ 2. Following class, or at the end of class if time allows, complete the Cadet Evaluation of Instructor form. As you respond, consider all of the lessons and related experiences that made up this Personal Development module.

1	**Exercise Title**	Problem Solving Exercise
2	**Exercise Number**	MSL301_L16_01C
3	**Type**	Worksheet
4	**Notes**	In-class exercise. Has two parts—MSL301_L16_01C and 01C2
5	**Purpose**	Apply the Army problem-solving process.

6 **Directions**

Working as a member of a small group, apply the Army problem-solving process to resolve the problem described in the situation below. Use a relative values decision matrix to help you solve this problem. Prepare a short briefing, for presentation to the class, of your solution and the thought process you used to develop your solution.

Situation

Cadet Tessa McMullen will graduate in less than two months and enter active Army service shortly after graduation. As she prepares for active duty, one of the most troubling decisions she is struggling with is trying to decide which vehicle she should buy. It is clear that her old car is nearing the end of its useful life and that it just does not have the carrying capacity she needs to support Army moves and her many outdoor pastimes. Tessa asked for your help in resolving the issue of which vehicle to buy. Given such a clearly defined problem, your next step was to gather information pertaining to the problem. You began by talking with Tessa to determine her vehicle needs and preferences.

Tessa told you that she had decided that she wanted to buy a sport utility vehicle. She believes that with the cargo capacity of an SUV, she can easily carry the many belongings she wants to have immediately available when she arrives at her first Army post. Tessa also engages in a variety of outdoor activities, including mountain biking, camping, windsurfing, and kayaking. She wants to make sure that her new SUV will carry her outdoor gear and allow her to drive on the rough dirt roads that lead to some of her favorite outdoor spots. Having a four-wheel drive capability and a strong engine would increase her confidence that she could reach her backcountry destinations and return with no problems.

Although Tessa likes to rough it in the outdoors, she also likes her creature comforts. Air-conditioning and a CD player are two features that her SUV must have. Even though she is able to competently drive a standard transmission vehicle, she does not particularly enjoy doing so. An automatic transmission would be welcome, although not essential. Finally, Tessa said that she would like to have a moon roof in her new vehicle because she enjoys the feeling of openness that it gives even when the weather is too cold to drive with it physically opened.

Cost, of course, is Tessa's main concern. She made it clear that she could not afford a monthly vehicle payment of more than $500, and that she would really like to keep the payment well below this amount. She has saved some money and could afford to put a down payment of up to $1,500 on the new vehicle, although spending this amount would stretch her budget and lengthen the time it would take to buy the many household items she will need for life on her own. Tessa also said that she would prefer to have her vehicle paid for by the time she reached the end of her 4-year initial active duty obligation.

After talking with Tessa, you used a reliable car information website to identify and gather information on several SUVs that you thought might be suitable for Tessa. You also prepared a spreadsheet showing monthly payments for different vehicle costs, interest rates, and loan durations. Phone calls to several banks revealed that the best interest rate that Tessa could hope for on a new car loan was 8 percent.

VEHICLE PAYMENTS FOR VARIOUS VEHICLE COSTS, INTEREST RATES, AND LOAN DURATIONS

Cost of Vehicle — Monthly Payment

Interest Rate	Duration (months)	$18,000	$19,000	$20,000	$21,000	$22,000	$23,000	$24,000	$25,000	$26,000	$27,000	$28,000
1.0%	12	$1,508.14	$1,591.92	$1,675.71	$1,759.49	$1,843.28	$1,927.06	$2,010.85	$2,094.64	$2,178.42	$2,262.21	$2,345.99
1.0%	24	$757.84	$799.94	$842.04	$884.14	$926.25	$968.35	$1,010.45	$1,052.55	$1,094.65	$1,136.76	$1,178.86
1.0%	36	$507.75	$535.95	$564.16	$592.37	$620.58	$648.79	$676.99	$705.20	$733.41	$761.62	$789.83
1.0%	48	$382.71	$403.97	$425.23	$446.49	$467.75	$489.01	$510.27	$531.54	$552.80	$574.06	$595.32
1.0%	60	$307.69	$324.78	$341.87	$358.97	$376.06	$393.16	$410.25	$427.34	$444.44	$461.53	$478.62
2.0%	12	$1,516.30	$1,600.54	$1,684.78	$1,769.02	$1,853.26	$1,937.49	$2,021.73	$2,105.97	$2,190.21	$2,274.45	$2,358.69
2.0%	24	$765.72	$808.27	$850.81	$893.35	$935.89	$978.43	$1,020.97	$1,063.51	$1,106.05	$1,148.59	$1,191.13
2.0%	36	$515.57	$544.21	$572.85	$601.49	$630.14	$658.78	$687.42	$716.06	$744.71	$773.35	$801.99
2.0%	48	$390.51	$412.21	$433.90	$455.60	$477.29	$498.99	$520.68	$542.38	$564.07	$585.77	$607.46
2.0%	60	$315.50	$333.03	$350.56	$368.08	$385.61	$403.14	$420.67	$438.19	$455.72	$473.25	$490.78
3.0%	12	$1,524.49	$1,609.18	$1,693.87	$1,778.57	$1,863.26	$1,947.96	$2,032.65	$2,117.34	$2,202.04	$2,286.73	$2,371.42
3.0%	24	$773.66	$816.64	$859.62	$902.61	$945.59	$988.57	$1,031.55	$1,074.53	$1,117.51	$1,160.49	$1,203.47
3.0%	36	$523.46	$552.54	$581.62	$610.71	$639.79	$668.87	$697.95	$727.03	$756.11	$785.19	$814.27
3.0%	48	$398.42	$420.55	$442.69	$464.82	$486.96	$509.09	$531.22	$553.36	$575.49	$597.63	$619.76
3.0%	60	$323.44	$341.41	$359.37	$377.34	$395.31	$413.28	$431.25	$449.22	$467.19	$485.15	$503.12
4.0%	12	$1,532.70	$1,617.85	$1,703.00	$1,788.15	$1,873.30	$1,958.45	$2,043.60	$2,128.75	$2,213.90	$2,299.05	$2,384.20
4.0%	24	$781.65	$825.07	$868.50	$911.92	$955.35	$998.77	$1,042.20	$1,085.62	$1,129.05	$1,172.47	$1,215.90
4.0%	36	$531.43	$560.96	$590.48	$620.00	$649.53	$679.05	$708.58	$738.10	$767.62	$797.15	$826.67
4.0%	48	$406.42	$429.00	$451.58	$474.16	$496.74	$519.32	$541.90	$564.48	$587.06	$609.63	$632.21
4.0%	60	$331.50	$349.91	$368.33	$386.75	$405.16	$423.58	$442.00	$460.41	$478.83	$497.25	$515.66
5.0%	12	$1,540.93	$1,626.54	$1,712.15	$1,797.76	$1,883.36	$1,968.97	$2,054.58	$2,140.19	$2,225.79	$2,311.40	$2,397.01
5.0%	24	$789.69	$833.56	$877.43	$921.30	$965.17	$1,009.04	$1,052.91	$1,096.78	$1,140.66	$1,184.53	$1,228.40
5.0%	36	$539.48	$569.45	$599.42	$629.39	$659.36	$689.33	$719.30	$749.27	$779.24	$809.21	$839.19
5.0%	48	$414.53	$437.56	$460.59	$483.62	$506.64	$529.67	$552.70	$575.73	$598.76	$621.79	$644.82
5.0%	60	$339.68	$358.55	$377.42	$396.30	$415.17	$434.04	$452.91	$471.78	$490.65	$509.52	$528.39
6.0%	12	$1,549.20	$1,635.26	$1,721.33	$1,807.40	$1,893.46	$1,979.53	$2,065.59	$2,151.66	$2,237.73	$2,323.79	$2,409.86
6.0%	24	$797.77	$842.09	$886.41	$930.73	$975.05	$1,019.37	$1,063.69	$1,108.02	$1,152.34	$1,196.66	$1,240.98
6.0%	36	$547.59	$578.02	$608.44	$638.86	$669.28	$699.70	$730.13	$760.55	$790.97	$821.39	$851.81
6.0%	48	$422.73	$446.22	$469.70	$493.19	$516.67	$540.16	$563.64	$587.13	$610.61	$634.10	$657.58
6.0%	60	$347.99	$367.32	$386.66	$405.99	$425.32	$444.65	$463.99	$483.32	$502.65	$521.99	$541.32

VEHICLE PAYMENTS FOR VARIOUS VEHICLE COSTS, INTEREST RATES, AND LOAN DURATIONS

Loan Information		Cost of Vehicle										
Interest Rate	Duration (months)	$18,000	$19,000	$20,000	$21,000	$22,000	$23,000	$24,000	$25,000	$26,000	$27,000	$28,000
		Monthly Payment										
7.0%	12	$1,557.48	$1,644.01	$1,730.53	$1,817.06	$1,903.59	$1,990.12	$2,076.64	$2,163.17	$2,249.70	$2,336.22	$2,422.75
7.0%	24	$805.91	$850.68	$895.45	$940.22	$985.00	$1,029.77	$1,074.54	$1,119.31	$1,164.09	$1,208.86	$1,253.63
7.0%	36	$555.79	$586.66	$617.54	$648.42	$679.30	$710.17	$741.05	$771.93	$802.80	$833.68	$864.56
7.0%	48	$431.03	$454.98	$478.92	$502.87	$526.82	$550.76	$574.71	$598.66	$622.60	$646.55	$670.49
7.0%	60	$356.42	$376.22	$396.02	$415.83	$435.63	$455.43	$475.23	$495.03	$514.83	$534.63	$554.43
8.0%	12	$1,565.79	$1,652.78	$1,739.77	$1,826.76	$1,913.75	$2,000.73	$2,087.72	$2,174.71	$2,261.70	$2,348.69	$2,435.68
8.0%	24	$814.09	$859.32	$904.55	$949.77	$995.00	$1,040.23	$1,085.45	$1,130.68	$1,175.91	$1,221.14	$1,266.36
8.0%	36	$564.05	$595.39	$626.73	$658.06	$689.40	$720.74	$752.07	$783.41	$814.75	$846.08	$877.42
8.0%	48	$439.43	$463.85	$488.26	$512.67	$537.08	$561.50	$585.91	$610.32	$634.74	$659.15	$683.56
8.0%	60	$364.98	$385.25	$405.53	$425.80	$446.08	$466.36	$486.63	$506.91	$527.19	$547.46	$567.74
9.0%	12	$1,574.13	$1,661.58	$1,749.03	$1,836.48	$1,923.93	$2,011.38	$2,098.84	$2,186.29	$2,273.74	$2,361.19	$2,448.64
9.0%	24	$822.33	$868.01	$913.69	$959.38	$1,005.06	$1,050.75	$1,096.43	$1,142.12	$1,187.80	$1,233.49	$1,279.17
9.0%	36	$572.40	$604.19	$635.99	$667.79	$699.59	$731.39	$763.19	$794.99	$826.79	$858.59	$890.39
9.0%	48	$447.93	$472.82	$497.70	$522.59	$547.47	$572.36	$597.24	$622.13	$647.01	$671.90	$696.78
9.0%	60	$373.65	$394.41	$415.17	$435.93	$456.68	$477.44	$498.20	$518.96	$539.72	$560.48	$581.23
10.0%	12	$1,582.49	$1,670.40	$1,758.32	$1,846.23	$1,934.15	$2,022.07	$2,109.98	$2,197.90	$2,285.81	$2,373.73	$2,461.64
10.0%	24	$830.61	$876.75	$922.90	$969.04	$1,015.19	$1,061.33	$1,107.48	$1,153.62	$1,199.77	$1,245.91	$1,292.06
10.0%	36	$580.81	$613.08	$645.34	$677.61	$709.88	$742.15	$774.41	$806.68	$838.95	$871.21	$903.48
10.0%	48	$456.53	$481.89	$507.25	$532.61	$557.98	$583.34	$608.70	$634.06	$659.43	$684.79	$710.15
10.0%	60	$382.45	$403.69	$424.94	$446.19	$467.43	$488.68	$509.93	$531.18	$552.42	$573.67	$594.92
11.0%	12	$1,590.87	$1,679.25	$1,767.63	$1,856.01	$1,944.40	$2,032.78	$2,121.16	$2,209.54	$2,297.92	$2,386.30	$2,474.69
11.0%	24	$838.94	$885.55	$932.16	$978.76	$1,025.37	$1,071.98	$1,118.59	$1,165.20	$1,211.80	$1,258.41	$1,305.02
11.0%	36	$589.30	$622.04	$654.77	$687.51	$720.25	$752.99	$785.73	$818.47	$851.21	$883.95	$916.68
11.0%	48	$465.22	$491.06	$516.91	$542.76	$568.60	$594.45	$620.29	$646.14	$671.98	$697.83	$723.67
11.0%	60	$391.36	$413.11	$434.85	$456.59	$478.33	$500.08	$521.82	$543.56	$565.30	$587.05	$608.79
12.0%	12	$1,599.28	$1,688.13	$1,776.98	$1,865.82	$1,954.67	$2,043.52	$2,132.37	$2,221.22	$2,310.07	$2,398.92	$2,487.77
12.0%	24	$847.32	$894.40	$941.47	$988.54	$1,035.62	$1,082.69	$1,129.76	$1,176.84	$1,223.91	$1,270.98	$1,318.06
12.0%	36	$597.86	$631.07	$664.29	$697.50	$730.71	$763.93	$797.14	$830.36	$863.57	$896.79	$930.00
12.0%	48	$474.01	$500.34	$526.68	$553.01	$579.34	$605.68	$632.01	$658.35	$684.68	$711.01	$737.35
12.0%	60	$400.40	$422.64	$444.89	$467.13	$489.38	$511.62	$533.87	$556.11	$578.36	$600.60	$622.84

MODULE III

The Army Profession:
Army Operations
(Part II)

Part II of The Army Profession:Army Operations module consists of lessons 17 through 24. These lessons build on the preceding Personal Development module (Problem Solving lessons 13 through 16) by examining the Army's adaptation of general problem solving and decision making principles to military operational problems and decisions. The lessons in Part II of this module take you through the eight steps of the troop leading procedure including mission analysis, planning, and execution. Sample missions are used throughout this module to give you practical experience in conducting the eight troop leading steps.

Troop Leading Procedures

This is a transition lesson between the Personal Development module on Problem Solving and the Army Operations module. This lesson is the first in a group of eight lessons dealing with military planning and the application of problem-solving principles to military operations. The purpose of this lesson is to show the relationship between troop leading procedures and the problem solving process. You will have worked in teams, have a basic familiarity with practices of problem-solving, and should be in a position to begin to integrate basic problem-solving skills with the specific steps and actions of the troop-leading procedures and military operations orders.

The following topics are addressed in this lesson:

- The eight troop leading procedures steps
- Relationship between troop leading procedures and the problem solving process
- Types and functions of military orders (warning order, operations order, & fragmentary order)
- The five paragraph OPORD structure and general content of each paragraph
- Military aspects of terrain

The following TLO is supported in whole or in part by this lesson:

- Conduct troop leading procedures

Following this lesson you will be able to:

- Describe the eight steps of the Army troop-leading procedure
- List the elements of METT-T
- Analyze the five military aspects of terrain according to OCOKA

CADET CHECKLIST

___ Go to Blackboard course site for MSL301-Lesson 17 and preview the lesson.

___ Complete the required readings and exercise:

    ___ 1. Read FM 7-8 *Infantry Rifle Platoon and Squad,* MAR 2001 (Chg 1), Chapter 2 page 2-1 through 2-23.

    ___ 2. Read FM 3-25.26 *Map Reading and Land Navigation,* JULY 2001, Chapter 11 page 11-9 through 11-12, and paragraph 11-4 Tactical Considerations.

    ___ 3. Scan FM 21-31 *Topographic Symbols,* DEC 1968 (Chg 1). Chapter 2, pages 5 through 86.

    ___ 4. Complete the Troop Leading Procedures pre-class Quiz.

OPTIONAL

    ___ 1. Following class, or at the end of class if time allows, complete either the *Reflection Feedback* or *Summary Review* form.

TROOP LEADING PROCEDURES PRE-CLASS QUIZ

INSTRUCTIONS

Based on the pre-class reading for this lesson, select the best answer for each of the questions below. Indicate your selection by circling it.

1. Which of the following is not true about the Army troop-leading procedure?
   A. It is a process that leaders use to prepare their units for tactical missions.
   B. It is the planning method usually used by squads and platoons.
   C. It contains eight steps, any of which can serve as the starting point.
   D. It is designed to give soldiers maximum preparation time.

2. Lieutenant Sylvester examined the order he had just received from his commander. He then called his platoon sergeant and squad leaders together to tell them about the new mission. He described the situation and mission to his subordinate leaders. He also outlined his initial concept of the operation, gave them individual tasks to accomplish, and a timeline for preparing for the mission. Lieutenant Sylvester has just issued:
   A. an operation plan.
   B. a mission briefing.
   C. a commander's intent statement.
   D. a warning order.

3. Key terrain is:
   A. a route that gives an attacking force the greatest protection and places the force at the enemy's most vulnerable spot.
   B. a location that allows good grazing fire as well as engagement of the enemy at the maximum effective range of organic weapons.
   C. a location or area whose seizure or retention affords a marked advantage to either combatant.
   D. terrain that both protects friendly forces from being seen and from being engaged by enemy direct and indirect fires.

4. The unit leader uses the acronym METT-T to:
   A. guide the estimate of the situation.
   B. analyze meteorological data affecting the mission.
   C. remember the elements of offensive operations.
   D. analyze the military aspects of terrain.

5. Among other things, the service support paragraph of an OPORD provides information about:
   A. the location of the unit supply vehicles.
   B. artillery units that will provide fires for the unit.
   C. the radio frequencies and call signs to be used.
   D. friendly units on the left and right flanks.

6. During the OPORD, Captain Tappan gave the mortar platoon leader a grid coordinate for the initial position of the mortars. CPT Tappan was issuing which paragraph of the OPORD?
   A. Paragraph 1—Situation
   B. Paragraph 2—Mission
   C. Paragraph 3—Execution
   D. Paragraph 4—Service Support

Receive Mission: METT-T

This is the second in a series of eight lessons on Troop Leading procedures within the Army Operations Module. This is the first in a two-part set on Mission analysis, METT-T. The purpose of this lesson is to have you analyze a Higher Headquarters (HQ) Operations Order and then extract specified tasks as well as constraints and limitations.

The following topics are addressed in this lesson:

- Identify specified, implied, and essential tasks from a higher headquarters OPORD
- Identify related constraints and limitations

The following TLO is supported in whole or in part by this lesson:

- Follow military planning considerations

Following this lesson you will be able to:

- Analyze a Higher HQ Operations order: Step one of the Troop Leading Procedures (Receive the Mission)
- Extract and classify tasks and limitations

CADET CHECKLIST

___ Go to Blackboard course site for MSL301-Lesson 18 and preview the lesson.

___ Complete the required reading:

    ___ 1. Read FM 7-8 *Light Infantry Platoon/Squad,* Chapter 2 pages 2-1 to 2-23.

OPTIONAL

    ___ 1. Following class, or at the end of class if time allows, complete either the *Reflection Feedback* or *Summary Review* form.

1	**Exercise Title**	Mission Analysis Worksheet
2	**Exercise Number**	MSL301_L18_02C
3	**Type**	Small Group Exercise
4	**Notes**	The West Point Map, Overlay, protractor, and Operations Order (OPORD) are necessary for lessons for MSL301-18, L19, L20, L21, L22, L23, and L24.
5	**Purpose**	It is designed to support the following enabling learning objectives: 1. Analyze a Higher HQ Operations Order: Step one of the TLP (Receive a Mission); and, 2. Extract and classify tasks and limitations.
6	**Directions**	

1. You are the Platoon Leader of 2nd Platoon, A Company, 2nd of the 81st Inf.

2. Analyze the mission using the Mission Analysis Worksheet below. Record the results of your analysis in the correct places below. Your small group will report the results to the large group.

3. You will need the following handouts to complete the exercise:

   • MSL301 West Point Map

   • MSL301 Overlay

   • MSL301 Defense Operations Order

   • Protractor

Step 1: Receive the Mission.

What is the MISSION?

What is known about the ENEMY?

How will TERRRAIN and WEATHER affect the operation?

What TROOPS are available?

How much TIME is available?

Are there CIVILIANS considerations?

WEST POINT AREA MAP

DEFENSE OPERATIONS ORDER

The time is now. 121800 JUL 2000

OPERATIONS ORDER A CO 1-00
References: 2-81 IN BN OPORD 1-00
West Point and Vicinity, New York V821S; Scale 1:25,000

Time Zone Used Throughout the Order: Romeo

Task Organization

1/A/2-81	2/A/2-81	3/A/2-81	Co HQ	1/1/C/226 EN
	AT Sect		FIST	
	60mm Mortars			

1. SITUATION.

    A. Enemy Forces.

        (1) *Disposition, Composition, and Strength*

           (a) *Disposition.* U.S. Forces are opposed by the Caquetan Liberty Brigade currently located 250 miles to our south. The enemy has capitalized on the introduction of U.S. forces into the country to rally support for their cause. Their regular forces are now augmented with recent inductees who are poorly trained. Liberty Brigade forces are expected to conduct reconnaissance operations to locate U.S. forces and identify vulnerabilities.

           (b) *Composition.* The Bde we are facing is composed of a mix of six light infantry companies and three mech infantry companies (equipped with Bradley Fighting Vehicles captured from government forces). They use their mechanized forces as a reserve. Each of the light infantry companies has two rifle plts and one plt of augmentees. The Caquetan regular light infantry plts are equipped with standard U.S. military equipment and include light mortar sections (two 60MM mortars) in each. Their light infantry is also equipped with modified civilian pick-up trucks. At full strength, each Caquetan regular rifle pltn will have approximately 34 soldiers equipped with a mix of M-16 rifles, M-249 style LMGs, M-60-style MGs, AT-4s, and 40MM grenade launchers. Enemy recon elements are equipped with state of the art night vision capability. Augmentee plts are not all outfitted in uniforms, but they are fully equipped with weapons. The mech companies have three plts with four M-2 BIFVs per plt and two M-2 BIFVs in the Co Hqs. The Caquetan logistics structure does not support the anti-tank capability of the BIFV, but they do have limited quantities of ammo for the 25MM chain-gun and a M-240-type coaxial machine gun. They have no tanks, no artillery, no ADA, and no aviation.

           (c) *Strength.* The enemy is estimated to be at approximately 80% personnel and 80% in equipment.

        (2) *Capabilities.* The Liberty Bde is capable of massing company-sized light infantry elements in less than 90 minutes (once their forces have entered our AO) to seize opportunities to destroy vulnerable forces. These light infantry forces are highly mobile, making use of modified civilian pick-up trucks—In fighting with government forces to date, they have been reluctant to dismount until absolutely necessary. They have also employed their mech reserves against the government forces to reinforce the success of committed light infantry units. In each case, they achieved overwhelming superiority to destroy the government forces and then quickly withdrew. They are expected to operate in small unit recon patrols of 4 to 9 men in order to gain intelligence on concentrations of U.S. forces. The morale of recent inductees ranges from fully supportive converts to the cause to those who were involuntarily impressed into service. With the introduction of

U.S. forces into their country, their regular forces are more committed than ever to the overthrow of the present government.

(3) *Enemy Most Probable Course of Action.* The Caquetan Liberty Bde Commander has repeatedly vowed that, if U.S. forces were introduced, he would immediately move to inflict maximum U.S. casualties. He expects that by doing so, he will gain popular support that will increase his recruitment effort and propel him into the domestic political forefront. The Bde is in the process of moving from their current stronghold 250 miles to our south. Their lead elements could enter our AO as early as midnight tonight. These elements are expected to probe our forward units to develop an estimate of our composition, disposition, and strength. Though their primary mission is recon, if possible, they will infiltrate to sabotage critical C2 and logistics nodes within the U.S. lodgement area in Newburgh (30 miles to our north). The enemy will follow their recon elements with attacks by pick-up truck mounted light infantry forces to destroy vulnerable U.S. elements.

(4) *Enemy Most Dangerous Course of Action.* The enemy attacks with a light infantry company to clear the SW-NE road network adjacent to Stoney Lonesome Brook and then reinforces that attack with their three mech infantry companies.

B. Friendly Forces.

(1) *Higher Unit's Mission.* 2–81 IN defends in sector from PL Hawk to PL Freedom NLT 141800JUL2000 with C Co forward and Alpha and Bravo Co's abreast in depth, in order to deny infiltration of enemy recon patrols, destroy enemy forces, and allow time for friendly mech forces to prepare for offensive operations. The Bn Commander's intent is to destroy enemy recon elements forward in sector. That's why C Co is to our front. B Co will defend forward in sector to deny enemy access to Highland Falls. The high ground in the western most part of our sector must also be denied to the enemy, shaping enemy efforts into the Stony Lonesome corridor, where A Company will destroy them in EA Lance. The battalion reserve, Co Tm Charlie, will be committed only to complete the destruction of enemy mech forces.

(2) *Left Unit's Mission.* B Company defends in sector to our left from PL Eagle to PL Osprey. They have been directed to defend forward to deny enemy light infantry access to Highland Falls.

(3) *Right Unit's Mission.* Our sister battalion, 2–47th Inf, defends in sector to our right from PL Hawk to PL Freedom. They have responsibility for the Hwy 293 corridor.

(4) *Front Unit's Mission.*

(a) C Co screens to our front from PL Hawk to PL Eagle to identify and destroy enemy recon elements and deny enemy use of Hwy 9W.

(b) Scout Plt screens forward of C Co to provide early warning. They will withdraw on order through B Co sector.

(5) *Rear Unit's Mission.* Bn maintains Co Team Charlie (12 M1A2 Tanks and 5 BFVs) in reserve initially vic TAA Hammer. Co Tm Charlie prepares to attack along axis Green to destroy enemy mech forces in EA Lance or along Axis Gold to destroy enemy mech forces in EA Longbow.

C. Attachments and Detachments. Task Organization effective 121800JUL2000.

2. MISSION. A Co defends in sector from PL Eagle [WA 859806 to WA 843817] to PL Osprey [WA 864822 to WA 853828] NLT 141800JUL2000 to deny infiltration of enemy recon elements, destroy light infantry forces, and if necessary, to defeat the enemy mech infantry battalion.

3. EXECUTION.

Commander's Intent. My intent is to move to our defensive positions ASAP, allowing maximum time for on-site preparation. We will aggressively patrol forward in sector to identify and destroy enemy recon elements. We will deny the enemy the use of the dismounted avenue of approach on the high ground in the western part of our sector, turning the enemy into the Stony Lonesome corridor. The concentrated fires of 2nd and 3rd platoons will destroy the enemy in EA Lance. This will allow time for friendly mech forces to prepare for offensive operations.

A. *Concept of the Operation.* We will defend with one plt forward to deny enemy recon and prevent the envelopment of our main effort, and two plts oriented on EA Lance.

B. *Maneuver:* Within 20 minutes of completion of this OPORD, we will initiate movement by dismounted Tactical Road March into our defensive sector approx 3Km southwest of our current location.   1st Plt, a supporting effort, defends from BP A1 vic WA 85758215 NLT 141800JUL2000 to deny enemy recon and prevent the envelopment of the company main effort. 2nd Plt, the main effort, defends from BP A2 vic WA 85588230 NLT 141800JUL2000 to destroy the enemy in EA Lance. 3rd Plt, a supporting effort, defends from BP A3 vic WA 85958230 NLT 141800JUL2000 to deny enemy recon efforts and assist in the destruction of the enemy in EA Lance.

C. *Fires:* 1/112 FA is DS to the Bn. C Co has priority of fires initially. 81mm Mortar Plt priority of fires to our 1st Plt initially, on order to our 2nd Plt. 2nd Plt is allocated the 81 MM FPF. Our 60mm Mortar Section will assist in fixing and destroying the enemy in EA Lance. Priority of 60mm fires, and FPF, is to 3rd Plt. Plts may submit a max of two planned targets to support their fire plan.

D. *Mobility/Counter-Mobility/Survivability:* 2nd PLT has priority of engineer effort initially, then 3rd.

E. *Tasks to Maneuver Units:*

   (1) 1st Plt. Occupy TAA vic WA 85958190. Occupy and defend from BP A1 vic WA 85758215 (see ops overlay) NLT 141800JUL2000. Ensure you maintain contact with C Co to our front and are tied in with 2–47 Inf on our right flank.

   (2) 2nd Plt. Main Effort. Occupy TAA vic WA 85358250. Occupy and defend from BP A2 vic WA 85588230 (see ops overlay) NLT 141800JUL2000.

   (3) 3rd Plt. Occupy TAA vic WA 86128245. Occupy and defend from BP A3 vic WA 85958230 (see ops overlay) NLT 141800JUL2000. Provide a fire team to assist the engineers from 0700–1900 in putting in the AT/AP minefields and wire obstacles in EA Lance.

F. *Tasks to Combat Support Units:*

   (1) 60 mm Mortar Sect. Opcon to 2nd Plt.

   (2) Anti-Armor Sect. Opcon to 2nd Plt.

   (3) 1/1/C 226 EN.
      (a) Emplace AT mine obstacles along western boundary of EA Lance (unimproved road network) and on Stony Lonesome Road.
      (b) Emplace a 100m AT/AP minefield in front of 2nd Plt, vic WA 85488212.
      (c) Provide all log cutting equipment to 1st Plt for use in preparing overhead cover.

G. *Coordinating Instructions:*

   (1) Co guides will assist each PLT into the TAAs. Order of march is 1st, Hq, 2nd, 3rd.

   (2) Submit request for planned tgts to the CP NLT 131200JUL2000.

   (2) PLs will each backbrief me prior to issuing your OPORDs. Include your plans for counter-recon patrols and other countermeasures. Plan 15 minutes for your backbrief.

   (3) All PLT sector sketches will be forwarded to Co CP NLT 1200 tomorrow.

   (4) Priorities of Work
      (a) 1st and 3rd Plts get LP/Ops out with eyes on Hwy 9W.
      (b) Develop the obstacles and fire plan for EA Lance.
      (c) Counter-Recon Patrols

(5) 1st and 3rd Plts conduct counter-recon patrols beginning 1900 tomorrow.

(4) PIR: Enemy Mortar Section locations, Enemy BFVs in any number (even 1).

(5) Engagement criteria. M-60s hold fire against recon elements unless friendly positions are in threat of being destroyed. In EA Lance: 1st Plt engages targets on Stoney Lonesome Road and south. 2nd Plt engages targets from north to south. Priority of AT fires to C2 vehicles.

(6) ADA weapons status Tight, Hold.

(7) Timeline:

Co OPORD	121800 JUL 2000
Initiate foot march to TAAs	121900 JUL 2000
Initial PL Back-briefs	122000 JUL 2000
PLT BPs occupied	130330 JUL 2000
PLT Sector Sketches complete	131300 JUL 2000
PL Back-briefs	131300 JUL 2000
Company Rehearsal	131900 JUL 2000
B/P to Defend NLT	141800 JUL 2000

4. SERVICE AND SUPPORT.

A. *General.* Combat Trains vic WA 85958170. Field Trains vic WA 86348236.

B. *Material and Services.*

(1) Class I. MREs and Water resupply will be pushed to PLT TAAs. Ration cycle is MRE, T, MRE.

(2) Class IV. In-country supplies of concertina are limited and lumber is non-existant. Each Plt will get 4 rolls of concertina and 200 sandbags in your push package along with the ammo. We will also push whatever pioneer tools we can to you as early as possible into your TAAs or defensive positions.

(3) Class V. Request resupply of M16, M203, M249, smoke grenades, and star clusters to restore basic loads. Twice Basic Loads for M-60s and frag grenades. Ammo resupply will be pushed to PLT BPs. Each Plt will also be pushed 40 M18 Claymore Mines and 6 AT-4s to Plt BPs. AT and AP mines will be pushed to BP A3 for use in EA Lance. 60mm HE will be pushed to BP A2.

(4) Class IX. Submit requests to restore battery basic loads per TACSOP.

C. *Medical:*

(1) Co CCP loc vic Co CP.

(2) Establish Plt CCPs and report locs to the Co CP NLT 131300JUL2000. Priority cases evacuated by helicopter if possible.

D. Co EPW Collection Point loc vic WA 85728240. Processing and evac per Bn SOP.

E. Bn Chaplain will be circulating within BPs A2 and A3 from 0630 to 0830 tomorrow.

F. Civil-Military Cooperation. Curfew for all civilians is at 1900.

5. COMMAND AND SIGNAL.

a. *Command:*

(1) Bn TAC loc initially vic WA 86008209. Bn TOC co-located with combat trains.

(2) Company CP located vic WA 85728240.

(3) Succession of command: XO, 2d Plt PL, 3rd Plt PL, 1st Plt PL, 1SG, 1st Plt PSG.

b. *Signal:*

   (1) Current SOI in effect. Daily change at 2400.

   (2) Running Password for returning patrols and OPs is Jackhammer. That will also be what C
       Co and the Scouts will use if they need to exfiltrate through our sector.

   (3) Radio listening silence until enemy contact. Wire is primary means of communications.

The time is now 121820 JUL 2000. I will be leaving in my HMMWV in 10 minutes to recon our sector. I have
room for 1 of you from each Plt.

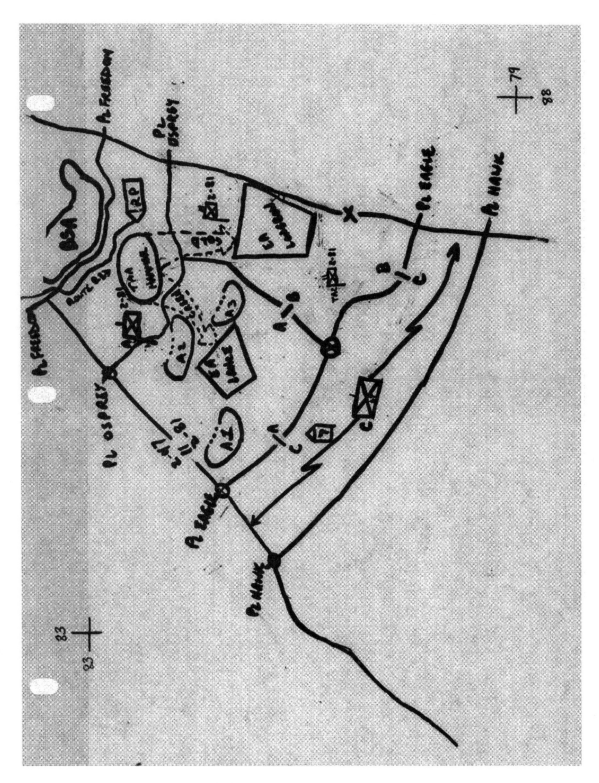

OPORD OPS OVERLAY

Mission Analysis

This is the third in a series of eight lessons on Troop Leading Procedures within the Army Operations module. This lesson continues the mission analysis phase of the military problem solving process introduced in the previous lesson. It focuses on terrain analysis and map reading.

The following topics are addressed in this lesson:

- METT-T analysis
- Military aspects of terrain (OKOCA)
- Time management for mission planning
- Restated Mission Statement

The following TLO is supported in whole or in part by this lesson:

- Follow military planning considerations

Following this lesson you will be able to:

- Analyze an order: Step one of the TLP (Receive the Mission)
- Use OKOCA to analyze Military Aspects of Terrain
- Write a Platoon Mission Statement

CADET CHECKLIST

___ Go to Blackboard course site for MS301-Lesson 19 and preview the lesson.

___ Complete the required reading:

    ___ 1. Read FM 7-8, *Infantry Rifle Platoon and Squad,* MAR 2001 (Chg 1), Chapter 2 pages 2-1 through 2-23 on the cadet CD.

OPTIONAL

    ___ 1. Review FM 21-31, *Topographic Symbols,* DEC 1968 (Chg 1), Chapter 2 on the cadet CD.

    ___ 2. Following class, or at the end of class if time allows, complete either the *Reflection Feedback* or *Summary Review* form.

1	**Exercise Title**	Terrain Analysis Worksheet
2	**Exercise Number**	MSL301_L19_01C
3	**Type**	Small Group Exercise
4	**Notes**	The West Point Map, Overlay, protractor, and Operations Order (OPORD) are necessary for lessons for MSL301-18, L19, L20, L21, L22, L23, and L24.
5	**Purpose**	It is designed to support the following enabling learning objectives for MSL301-L19: 1. Analyze an order: Step one of the TLP (Receive the Mission); 2. Analyze Military Aspects of Terrain using OKOCA; and, 3. Write a Platoon Mission Statement.

6 Directions

1. You are the Platoon Leader of 2nd Platoon, A Company, 2nd of the 81st Inf.

2. Analyze the terrain using OCOKA and this Terrain Analysis Worksheet. Record the results of your analysis in the locations provided below. OCOKA will provide the information for the Terrain and Weather portion of METT-T.

3. Revise your Mission Analysis Worksheet (MSL301_L18_01C) as required and prepare to report the results to the large group.

4. You will need the following handouts to complete the exercise:

   • MSL301 West Point Map

   • MSL301 Overlay

   • MSL301 Defense Operations Order

   • Protractor

(O) Observation and fields of fire

(C) Cover and concealment

(O) Obstacles

(K) Key terrain

(A) Avenues of Approach

In considering the effects of weather, visibility and trafficability are the most important concern.

Issue Warning Order

This is the fourth in a series of eight lessons on Troop Leading procedures within the Army Operations module. This lesson focuses on step two of the Troop Leading Procedures, issuance of a warning order. During this lesson, you will use the five-paragraph OPORD format to develop warning orders. You will practice creating warning orders for scenarios that also reinforce understanding of OCOKA.

The following topic is addressed in this lesson:

- Preparation of a warning order

The following TLO is supported in whole or in part by this lesson:

- Conduct Troop Leading Procedures

Following this lesson you will be able to:

- Relate Step 1 of the TLP to Step 2
- Use mission analysis to develop the basis for a warning order
- Issue a warning order

CADET CHECKLIST

____ Go to Blackboard course site for MSL301-Lesson 20 and preview the lesson.

____ Complete the required reading:

    ____ 1. Read FM 7-8 *Infantry Rifle Platoon and Squad,* MAR 2001 (Chg 1), Chapter 2 pages 2-1 through 2-23 on the cadet CD.

OPTIONAL

    ____ 1. Following class, or at the end of class if time allows, complete either the *Reflection Feedback* or *Summary Review* form.

1	**Exercise Title**	Issue a Warning Order Worksheet
2	**Exercise Number**	MSL301_L20_01C
3	**Type**	Small Group Exercise
4	**Notes**	The West Point Map, Overlay, protractor, and Operations Order (OPORD) are necessary for lessons for MSL301-18, L19, L20, L21, L22, L23, and L24.
5	**Purpose**	It is designed to support the following enabling learning objectives (ELO's) of MSL301 Lesson 20 Relate Step 1 of the TLP to Step 2 Use mission analysis to develop the basis for a warning order Issue a Warning Order: Step 2 of the TLP
6	**Directions**	

1. You are the Platoon Leader of 2nd Platoon, A Company, 2nd of the 81st Inf.

2. Analyze the information in all previous handouts and worksheets to prepare and issue a warning order. Someone from your small group will issue the group's warning order to the large group.

3. The warning order has no specific format. If available, the following information should be included in a warning order:

   ■ The mission or nature of the operation

   ■ Who is participating in the operation

   ■ Time of the operation

   ■ Time and place for issuing the OPORD

Make a Tentative Plan

This is the fifth in a series of eight lessons on Troop Leading procedures within the Army Operations module. This lesson focuses on step three of the Troop Leading Procedures, make a tentative plan. This lesson builds on your familiarization with OCOKA and the practice of issuing warning orders.

The following topics are addressed in this lesson:

- Develop Courses of Action
- Analyze and Compare Courses of Action
- Select a course of action and develop a tentative plan

The following TLO is supported in whole or in part by this lesson:

- Conduct troop leading procedures

Following this lesson you will be able to:

- List the four steps of The Estimate of the Situation
- Explain how mission analysis contributes to development of the tentative plan
- Develop a tentative plan for a platoon defensive operation

CADET CHECKLIST

___ Go to Blackboard course site for MSL301-Lesson 21 and preview the lesson.

___ Complete the required reading:

___ 1. FM 7-8 *Light Infantry Platoon/Squad,* Chapter 2 pages 2-27 to 2-53 and Section III, on the cadet CD.

OPTIONAL

___ 1. Following class, or at the end of class if time allows, complete either the *Reflection Feedback* or *Summary Review* form.

1	**Exercise Title**	Make Tentative Plan Worksheet
2	**Exercise Number**	MSL301_L21_01C
3	**Type**	Small Group Exercise
4	**Notes**	The West Point Map, Overlay, protractor, and Operations Order (OPORD) are necessary for lessons for MSL301-18, L19, L20, L21, L22, L23, and L24.
5	**Purpose**	At the end of this lesson the cadet should be able to list the steps in the military decision making process used to develop a tentative plan, explain how mission analysis contributes to development of the tentative plan, and develop a tentative plan for a platoon using the five step planning process.

6	**Directions**	*Notes*
	1. You are the Platoon Leader of 2nd Platoon, A Company, 2nd of the 81st Inf.	
	2. Analyze the information in all previous handouts and worksheets to prepare and formulate a tentative plan. Someone from your small group will brief the group's tentative plan to the large group.	
	3. Develop an estimate of the situation:	
	a. Conduct detailed mission analysis	
	b. Conduct a situation analysis	
	c. Develop courses of action	
	d. Analyze each course of action	

e. Compare each course of action

f. Select a course of action

4. Refine the plan

Movement, Recon, and Complete Plan

This is the sixth in a series of eight lessons on Troop Leading procedures within the Army Operations module. It builds on the foundations set out in the previous lesson involving the formulation of a tentative plan. This lesson is designed to familiarize you with steps four through six of the troop leading procedures. It addresses the purpose, supervision, and execution of movement in the absence of the primary unit (squad/platoon) leader; the purpose and execution of a map or ground reconnaissance; and completion of the OPORD in light of mission updates and the results of the reconnaissance.

The following topics are addressed in this lesson:

- Purpose, supervision, and execution of preparatory unit movement
- Purpose, methods, and execution of map and ground reconnaissance
- Considerations in the completion of the OPORD

The following TLO is supported in whole or in part by this lesson:

- Conduct troop leading procedures

Following this lesson you will be able to:

- Describe when and under what circumstances to initiate movement and recon
- Identify the steps to develop a plan
- Develop a complete plan

CADET CHECKLIST

____ Go to Blackboard course site for MSL301-Lesson 22 and preview the lesson.

____ Complete the required reading:

    ____ 1. FM 7-8 *Light Infantry Platoon/Squad,* Chapter 2 pages 2-38 through 2-53 on the cadet CD.

OPTIONAL

    ____ 1. Following class, or at the end of class if time allows, complete either the *Reflection Feedback* or *Summary Review* form.

1	**Exercise Title**	Complete the Plan
2	**Exercise Number**	MSL301_L22_01C
3	**Type**	Small Group Exercise Worksheet
4	**Notes**	The West Point Map, Overlay, protractor, and Operations Order (OPORD) are necessary for lessons for MSL301-18, L19, L20, L21, L22, L23, and L24.
5	**Purpose**	At the end of this lesson the cadet should be able to describe when and under what circumstances to initiate movement and recon and develop a complete plan.

6	**Directions**	*NOTES:*

Directions

1. You are the Platoon Leader of 2nd Platoon, A Company, 2nd of the 81st Inf.

2. Analyze the information in all previous handouts and worksheets to complete the plan. Someone from your small group will brief the group's completed plan to the large group.

3. Do you have the time to conduct a personal reconnaissance? Can you get by without it?

4. When should you start moving the platoon forward?

5. Complete the plan you started in Lesson 18 by answering the six questions listed below and record your completed plan on the second page of the worksheet.

    1. State the MISSION.

    2. Describe what is known about the ENEMY.

    3. Explain how TERRAIN and WEATHER will affect the operation.

    4. Identify the TROOPS that are available.

    5. State how much TIME is available.

    6. List the CIVILIAN considerations.

COMPLETED PLAN

Issue Operations Order

This is the seventh in a series of eight lessons on Troop Leading procedures within the Army Operations module. The purpose of this lesson is to have you apply what you learned from previous lessons about gathering information, analyzing the situation, including constraints and limitations. Guided by the instructor, you will complete a final operations order and deliver the order to subordinates.

The following topics are addressed in this lesson:

- Prepare an operations order
- Prepare OPORD briefing aids (sketches, overlays, terrain models, etc.)
- Issue an operations order
- Receive and correct an OPORD brief-back from a subordinate

The following TLO is supported in whole or in part by this lesson:

- Conduct troop leading procedures

Following this lesson you will be able to:

- Identify when and under what circumstances to issue an operations order
- List the characteristics of an operations order
- Issue an operations order

CADET CHECKLIST

___ Go to Blackboard course site for MSL301-Lesson 23 and preview the lesson.

___ Complete the required reading:

    ___ 1. Review FM 7-8 *Light Infantry Platoon/Squad*, Chapter 2 pages 2-10 through 2-23 on the cadet CD.

OPTIONAL

    ___ 1. Following class, or at the end of class if time allows, complete either the *Reflection Feedback* or *Summary Review* form.

1	**Exercise Title**	Issue the Operations Order
2	**Exercise Number**	MSL301_L23_01C
3	**Type**	Small Group Exercise
4	**Notes**	The West Point Map, Overlay, protractor, and Operations Order (OPORD) are necessary for lessons for MSL301-18, L19, L20, L21, L22, L23, and L24.
5	**Purpose**	At the end of this lesson the cadet will be able to identify when and under what circumstances to issue an operations order, list the characteristics of an operations order, and issue an operations order.
6	**Directions**	

1. You are the Platoon Leader of 2nd Platoon, A Company, 2nd of the 81st Inf.

2. Analyze the information in all previous handouts and worksheets to issue the complete oral OPORD. Be prepared to issue the oral OPORD based on your completed plan.

3. Rehearse the oral OPORD for the time provided by the instructor. Prepare a sketch using available materials.

   ■ Issue the order within sight of the objective or on the defensive terrain.

   ■ When this is not possible, you should use a terrain model or sketch.

   ■ Be sure that your subordinates understand the mission, the commander's intent, the concept of the operation, and their assigned tasks.

   ■ Require your subordinates to repeat all or part of the order or demonstrate on the model or sketch their understanding of the operation.

   ■ Quiz the soldiers to ensure that all understand the mission.

Supervise, Inspect, and Rehearse

This is the last in a series of eight lessons on Troop Leading procedures within the Army Operations module. The purpose of this lesson is to have you take what you learned from previous Troop Leading Procedures and apply it in issuing orders and preparing the platoon to carry out those orders. You will also integrate what you have learned in Leadership Labs and practice sessions so that you can carry out inspections and required rehearsals.

The following topics are addressed in this lesson:

- Purpose, planning, and execution of pre-operational rehearsals
- Purpose, focus, and execution of pre-operational inspections

The following TLO is supported in whole or in part by this lesson:

- Conduct Troop Leading Procedures

Following this lesson you will be able to:

- List characteristics of supervision
- Identify those items in the approved plan that need to be inspected
- Identify those items in the approved plan that need to be rehearsed
- Summarize the steps involved in Troop Leading Procedures

CADET CHECKLIST

___ Go to Blackboard course site for MS301-Lesson 24 and preview the lesson.

___ Complete the required reading:

___ 1. Review FM 7-8 *Light Infantry Platoon/Squad,* Chapter 2 pages 2-3 through 2-10 on the cadet CD.

OPTIONAL

___ 1. Following class, or at the end of class if time allows, complete either the *Reflection Feedback* or *Summary Review* form.

___ 2. Following class, or at the end of class if time allows, complete the *Cadet Evaluation of Instructor* form. As you respond, consider all of the lessons and related experiences that made up this module, The Army Profession: Army Operations

1	**Exercise Title**	Supervise, Inspect, and Rehearse
2	**Exercise Number**	MSL301_L24_01C
3	**Type**	Individual Exercise
4	**Notes**	The West Point Map, Overlay, protractor, and Operations Order (OPORD) are necessary for lessons for MSL301-18, L19, L20, L21, L22, L23, and L24.
5	**Purpose**	At the end of this lesson the cadet will be able to identify those items in the approved plan that need to be inspected, identify those items in the approved plan that need to be rehearsed, and summarize the steps involved in Troop Leading Procedures.

6	**Directions**	*NOTES*
	1. You are the Platoon Leader of 2nd Platoon, A Company, 2nd of the 81st Inf.	
	2. Analyze the information in all previous handouts and worksheets to identify those items you should inspect or rehearse as time permits.	
	■ Things to inspect:	
	■ Things to rehearse:	

1	**Exercise Title**	Troop Leading Procedures Summary Review (SR)
2	**Exercise Number**	MSL301_L24SRC
3	**Type**	Summary Review
4	**Notes**	A Summary Review (SR) is a professional discussion of an event, focused on performance standards. A SR enables cadets to discover for themselves what worked, what failed to work, and how to improve the situation next time. This is a tool for continuous improvement. It gives the cadet the opportunity to reflect upon any insight, observations, or lessons learned from the activity or event.
5	**Purpose**	The purpose of this set of lessons is to teach cadets the eight steps of the Troop Leading Procedures and have them apply the procedures to issue orders and prepare the platoon to carry out those orders.

6   Directions

1. Summarize in writing what you have learned in the eight lessons on Troop Leading Procedures (MSL301_L17 through MSL301_L24).

2. Hand in the completed Summary Review to the instructor before you leave the classroom.

MODULE IV

The Army Profession: Officership

This module consists of twelve lessons that focus on The Army Profession, and Officership. The first seven lessons, 25 through 31, provide an extensive examination of the unique purpose, roles, and obligations of commissioned officers. This series of lessons covers history, source documents, organizational structure, and the Army's source of authority—the Congress. The aim is to convey a clear and complete understanding of what it means to be a commissioned officer. Special emphasis is given to the officer's role in shaping and guiding the growth and evolution of the Army through decisions, policies, and personal example.

Lessons 32 through 36 consist of a series of case studies, designed to enable you to examine the Officer Corps and the Evolution of the United States Army from Vietnam and the years following to its emerging strength during the Gulf War. The case studies focus on how organizations change and the important role leaders play in effecting change for the better in the Army.

By tracing the successes and failures of the force as it evolved from the Vietnam War to the present, the previous Army Profession and Officership lessons topics are placed in a real-world context that directly affect your future.

Each of the lessons that make up this case study cover a specific phase of the Army's evolution: The Vietnam War, The Army of the 70's, The Transformation, Desert Shield/Desert Storm, and Into the Twenty First Century. Identifying and tracing the critical elements of the transformation phase serves as the mechanism by which the various phases are tied together. Nine of these critical elements are then used as threads of continuity by which you trace the evolution of the Army and the responsibilities, influences, successes, and failures of the officer corps. These nine threads of continuity include: quality of people, war fighting doctrine, force structure, continuous modernization, leader development, empowerment of the NCO Corps, integration of reserve forces, and institutional values.

Foundations of Officership

This is the first of a series of seven lessons on the Army Profession and Officership. This series of lessons covers history, source documents, organizational structure, and the Army's source of authority—the Congress. Specifically, this lesson addresses the obligations and the legal basis of the commissioned officer corps through an examination of the United States Constitution, the Officers Commission, and the Oath of Office.

The following topics are addressed in this lesson:

- Army officer traditions
- The Constitution, commission, and oath of office as they relate to officers
- Legal responsibilities of officers
- The Army Profession and Officership through history

The following TLO is supported in whole or in part by this lesson:

- Relate the characteristics of a profession to military service as an officer

Following this lesson you will be able to:

- Identify the source of the authority to commission officers
- Identify the source of Commissioned Officers' authority
- Identify the source of the Commissioned Officers Oath
- Summarize the officers commission
- Summarize the Oath of Office

CADET CHECKLIST

___ Go to Blackboard course site for MS301-Lesson 25 and preview the lesson.

___ Complete the required readings and exercise:

    ___ 1. Scan the *Preface of the Army Officers Guide* located in the cadet textbook.

    ___ 2. Review *The Oath of Office for Commissioned Officers* in the cadet textbook.

    ___ 3. Review *The Officers Commission* (DD Form 1A) in the cadet textbook.

    ___ 4. Review FM 22-100, *Army Leadership: Be, Know, Do,* AUG 1999. Appendix F, *The Constitution of the United States.* Article I, Section 8 and Article II, Sections 2 and 3 on the cadet CD.

    ___ 5. Complete the pre-class worksheet. Take notes and answer questions related to the readings.

    ___ 6. Read the vignette in this workbook on General Washington at Newburgh in preparation for the in-class exercise.

OPTIONAL

    ___ 1. Read *How Militaries Transform–Various Schools of Thought.*

    ___ 2. Following class, or at the end of class if time allows, complete either the *Reflection Feedback* or *Summary Review* form.

PRE-CLASS ACTIVITY WORKSHEET

READING

Review the readings. Use the following worksheet to take notes as you read.

I. THE CONSTITUTION

Review the United States Constitution. Read the following sections.

 a. Article 1, Section 8.
 b. Article 2, Section 2, and Section 3.

Discussion questions

When reading the selected articles of the Constitution, be prepared to answer the following questions in class:

 a. Who has the authority to declare war?

 b. Who has the responsibility to raise and support Armies?

 c. What are some of the other responsibilities of Congress as outlined in Article I, Section 8 of the Constitution?

 d. Who is the Commander in chief of the Army and Navy, and where does he get this authority?

 e. Article II, Section 3 lists several responsibilities of the President, one of which is key to this class's discussion.

II. THE OFFICER'S COMMISSION

Read the Officer's Commission.

The President of the United States of America, to all who shall see these presents greeting:

Know ye that, reposing special trust and confidence in the patriotism, valor, fidelity, and abilities of (Name of Officer), I do appoint him/her a Second Lieutenant in the Army Reserve of the United States Army, to rank as such from the (date of commissioning). This officer will therefore carefully and diligently discharge the duties of the office to which appointed by doing and performing all manner of things hereunto belonging.

And I do strictly charge and require those officers and other personnel of lesser rank to render such obedience as is due an officer of this grade and position. And, this officer is to observe and follow such orders and directions from time to time as may be given by the president of the United States of America or other superior officers acting in accordance with the laws of the United States of America.

This commission is to continue in force during the pleasure of the President of the United States of America, under the provisions of those public laws relating to officers of the Armed Forces of the United States of America and the component thereof in which this appointment is made.

Done at the City of Washington this Xx day of (Month) in the year of our Lord, Two Thousand Xxxx Xxxx, and of the Independence of the United States of America, the Two Hundred and Xxxx Xxxx.

2. Discussion questions

a. Where does the commission come from?

Note: Do not prepare detailed answers, just jot down a few key words to help you participate in a class discussion.

b. What do the following terms mean:

special trust and confidence—

patriotism—

valor—

fidelity—

abilities—

c. What does it mean when the commission states

■ "This officer will therefore carefully and diligently discharge the duties of the office to which appointed by doing and performing all manner of things hereunto belonging. (i.e. what are some of these duties of the office, what would be some of the things hereunto belonging).

■ "And I do strictly charge and require those officers and other personnel of lesser rank to render such obedience as is due an officer of this grade and position." (i.e. where does a new lieutenant fit in, how are "persons of lesser rank" referred to?)

■ "And, this officer is to observe and follow such orders and directions from time to time as may be given by the president of the United States of America or other superior officers acting in accordance with the laws of the United States of America." (i.e. how does this relate to the Constitution?)

■ "This commission is to continue in force during the pleasure of the President of the United States of America, under the provisions of those public laws relating to officers of the Armed Forces of the United States of America and the component thereof in which this appointment is made." (i.e. what happens when a new president is elected, what are the "public laws" referred to?)

III. THE OATH OF OFFICE

Read the Officers Oath of Office

I, *having been appointed an officer in the Army of the United States, in the grade of second lieutenant, do solemnly swear that I will support and defend the Constitution of the United States against all enemies, foreign and domestic; that I will bear true faith and allegiance to the same; that I take this obligation freely, without any mental reservation or purpose of evasion, and that I will well and faithfully discharge the duties of the office upon which I am about to enter, so help me God.*

2. What do each of the following parts of the oath mean?

   a. Support and defend the constitution of the United States against all enemies, foreign and domestic;

   b. Bear true faith and allegiance to the same;

   c. That I take this obligation freely, without any mental reservation or purpose of evasion, and that I will well and faithfully discharge the duties of the office upon which I am about to enter.

1	**Exercise Title**	General Washington at Newburgh, New York Worksheet
2	**Exercise Number**	MSL301_L25_02C
3	**Type**	Question-and-Answer vignette and worksheet
4	**Notes**	
5	**Purpose**	Use the role model of General Washington at Newburgh New York to understand key aspects of the traditions of leadership, officership, and the relation of the Army to the Congress.

6 Directions

1. Form in to groups of three to six cadets.

2. Review the attached vignette and discussion questions.

3. You will be given 10 minutes to review the materials, go over the discussion questions, talk among yourselves, reach conclusion about your responses to the questions, and develop a brief report. Use the flipchart to present your responses. Designate one cadet to do the reporting. After 5 minutes have elapsed, your instructor will provide a five-minute warning to the class, followed by a 1 minute warning, and completion of the exercise.

   Note: This is the same reading you had as part of your class preparation.

4. At the end of the 10 minutes, your instructor will call on each group to present its conclusions.

READING—GENERAL WASHINGTON AT NEWBURGH

By early 1783, active hostilities of the American Revolutionary War had been over for nearly two years and commissioners were still in Paris to establish a final treaty with Great Britain. With no fighting to do, the Continental army had grown bored and restless, but Congress had decided to retain it as long as the British remained in New York to ensure that the gains of seven years of fighting would not be lost.

Disillusionment and doubt had been building among many officers of the army, then headquartered at Newburgh, New York. Born out of this growing loss of morale and confidence was a conspiracy to undertake a coup d'etat and establish a military dictatorship for the young United States.

Many officers had let their personal affairs during the war fall into great disarray, and unless they soon received a bonus or substantial payment of back wages, had nothing to look forward to upon returning home except imprisonment for failing to pay their accumulated debts. Washington worried that a failure to pay the troops would set loose "a train of evils."

In November of 1782, a group of officers headed by Major Gen. Henry Knox, with Washington's encouragement, drafted a petition of grievances to present to the Congress.

To ensure that Congress would receive and give prompt attention to their petition, the officers selected a committee of three, headed by Major Gen. Alexander McDougall, to carry it to Philadelphia in December 1782. Shortly after the committee's arrival, several prominent politicians who were later to become leaders in the Federalist faction sought out McDougall and advised him and his committee to begin a strenuous lobbying effort to point out to Congress, the shameful conditions in the army and the ire of its officers. The small group of Federalists also encouraged McDougall to alert all the officers at Newburgh to begin preparing for action beyond petitioning. Thus, "the terror of a mutinying army" was used to attempt to influence important members of Congress.

At first, the lobbying effort seemed to be succeeding. However, certain unfortunate snags also began to occur. Knox failed to produce requested evidence of deterioration of morale, and some legislators began to suspect the army was being used to twist arms. Well aware that Washington would have no part in this attempt to intimidate the Congress, the plotters decided to approach Henry Knox, Washington's chief of artillery who was in sympathy with Federalist aims, had openly complained about Congress, and enjoyed Washington's trust. However, Knox saw clearly that this amounted to nothing less than mutiny, and refused to help. As he said, "I consider the reputation of the American army as one of the most immaculate things on earth." In his estimation, the officers should suffer almost any wrong rather than bring discredit upon the Army in any form.

As luck would have it, a high-ranking weak link did exist. Maj. Gen. Horatio Gates, who previously tried to replace Washington, still possessed some political influence. He was also second in command at Newburgh.

One of his former aides, Col. Walter Stewart, met with Gates at his official residence, scathingly critical of both Congress and Washington. Gates, still smarting from his failure to discredit and oust Washington, saw a potential opportunity to even the score. Thus were laid plans aimed at the removal of Washington as well as for a military takeover of the Congress and the country. By early January 1783 Gates was in touch with those in Philadelphia whom he thought would support the plan.

However, Gates, along with several others, was being deceived and used. The devious Federalist faction in Philadelphia was fanning the fire of rebellion with one hand and trying to douse it with water with the other. What they wanted was an unsuccessful uprising of the army, enough to secure their will in Congress but stopping well short of complete anarchy or military dictatorship. They were playing a dangerous chess game in which Gates, Washington, Congress and the army were to be the pawns.

Washington found himself in a dilemma. Should he support his officers and the army and guide this nascent movement to correct obvious wrongs? Or was his first duty to Congress? Like Knox, Washington made a momentous decision: He would not lead what he considered an improper and irregular attempt to rectify those egregious wrongs.

A notice was circulated inviting all field-grade and company level officers to a meeting on March 10 to consider these issues. As this meeting was against regulations, it implied a casting-off of Washington's leadership and the taking of drastic action. A further message suggested that the officers should not disband until they had obtained "justice" and also implied that Gen. Washington was secretly in favor of such an act, but because of his position could not take an open stand. Thus, the officers should not worry about disregarding Washington's public stance and acting independently.

Washington, upon receiving and reading copies of these circulating communications smacking of mutiny, trembled with anger and shock. Shaking off his momentary astonishment, he immediately began the task of defusing the planned rebellion. To gain time, he canceled the illicit March 10 meeting and rescheduled it with one for March 15. He secured the support of influential subordinates, including Henry Knox, to back him in the upcoming confrontation and to keep him abreast of developments in camp. He sent messages to Congress to apprise them of the situation. All the while, he was carefully preparing a set of remarks to be presented to the meeting, ostensibly not by himself but by a high-ranking subordinate.

By late morning of March 15, Gen. Gates, acting as chairman in Washington's absence, opened the meeting. Suddenly, a small door off the stage swung open and in strode Gen. Washington. He asked to speak to the assembled officers, and the stunned Gates had no recourse but to comply with the request. As Washington surveyed the sea of faces before him, he no longer saw respect or deference as in times past, but *saw suspicion, irritation, and even unconcealed anger.* To such a hostile crowd, Washington was about to present the most crucial speech of his career.

Following his address Washington studied the faces of his audience. He could see that they were still confused, uncertain, not quite appreciating or comprehending what he was about to do or say. With a sigh, he removed from his pocket a letter and announced it was from a member of Congress, and that he now wished to read it to them. He produced the letter, gazed upon it, manipulated it without speaking. What was wrong, some of the men wondered. Why did he delay? Washington now reached into a pocket and brought out a pair of new reading glasses. Only those nearest to him knew he lately required them, and he had never worn them in public. Then he spoke: *"Gentlemen, you will permit me to put on my spectacles, for I have not only grown gray but almost blind in the service of my country."* As he read the letter to their un-listening ears, many were in tears from the recollections and emotions which flooded their memories. Finishing, Washington carefully and deliberately folded the letter, took off his glasses, and exited briskly from the hall. Immediately, Knox and others faithful to Washington offered resolutions affirming their appreciation for their commander in chief, and pledging their patriotism and loyalty to the Congress, deploring and regretting those threats and actions which had been uttered and suggested.

DISCUSSION QUESTIONS

a. Was the Officer Corps right in how they acted? Why or why not?

b. Could such a thing happen today? Why or why not?

c. How does this incident relate to the officer of today?

d. As a group, capture your initial impression in a single sentence of the following individuals:

1) General Washington—

2) General Gates—

3) General Knox—

BRIEFING

a. Prepare your answers to the questions in "bullet" format.

b. List your responses on flipchart paper and be prepared to discuss.

Officer Duties

This is the second of a series of seven lessons on the Army Profession and Officership. Whereas the first lesson focused on the Army's source of authority and laid historical foundations for the authority and role of the officer, this lesson expands on moral duties and responsibilities of officership.

The following topics are addressed in this lesson:

- The social contract and expectation of selfless service
- The nobility of profession
- Duty, Honor, Country
- The concept of officership as a unique calling in society

The following TLO is supported in whole or in part by this lesson:

- Relate the characteristics of a profession to military service as an officer

Following this lesson you will be able to:

- List the basic duties of an officer
- Describe and give examples of Duty, Honor, Country
- Explain how the concept of Duty, Honor, Country is significant

CADET CHECKLIST

___ Go to Blackboard course site for MSL301-Lesson 26 and preview the lesson.

___ Complete the required readings and exercises:

    ___ 1. Read *The Commander's Concept of Duty* in the textbook.

    ___ 2. Read MacArthur's speech. This historic speech is part of the foundation for the Army's concepts of Duty, Honor, and Country as they apply to the Officer Corps in the textbook or list to it at *http://www.west-point.org/real/macarthur_address.html*.

    ___ 3. Find an example of self-sacrifice in the news and bring to class. Refer to pre-class *Self-Sacrifice Worksheet* assignment.

    ___ 4. Complete the *Self-Sacrifice Worksheet*.

OPTIONAL

    ___ 1. Preview the in-class activity using the *Duty and Honor Worksheet*.

    ___ 2. Following class, or at the end of class if time allows, complete either the *Reflection Feedback* or *Summary Review* form.

1	**Exercise Title**	Self-Sacrifice
2	**Exercise Number**	MSL301_L26_01C
3	**Type**	Worksheet
4	**Notes**	
5	**Purpose**	Research and discover examples of heroic courage, self-sacrifice and bravery.
6	**Directions**	

Think about what it is to be a hero. For example, there were many heroes and many kinds of heroes who sacrificed themselves for the good of others as a result of the 9/11 terrorist attack. Throughout history soldiers have exhibited personal courage and selfless service. Go to your library, search the web, or check out your local newspaper for the stories of personal self-sacrifice. Select one. Write out a brief paragraph. Answer the following questions. Be sure to bring this activity to class for discussion.

1. Who is your example of heroic self-sacrifice?

2. When did he or she live?

3. What action did he or she take that merits your recognition?

4. What is it about this person that you admire?

1	**Exercise Title**	Honor and Duty
2	**Exercise Number**	MSL301_L26_02C
3	**Type**	Worksheet
4	**Notes**	
5	**Purpose**	Formulate a personal statement of honor and duty. Relate them to Army traditions of honor and duty.

6	**Directions**

When you hear the word honor, what is the first image that comes to mind? Answer the questions below. Then write a brief summary of what your idea of personal honor is. How do you plan to live a life of honor?

Go through the same set of questions—this time related to the idea of Duty.

Honor

1. Name three people (real or fictional) you consider to be honorable.

2. Describe three acts you believe to be honorable.

3. Name one thing you did in the past year that you believe was honorable.

4. What are the key characteristics of honor that you prize most?

5. How does your sense of Honor compare with General MacArthur's?

Duty

1. Name three people (real or fictional) whom you consider to do their duty.

2. Describe three acts you believe to respect the code of duty.

3. Name one thing you did in the past year that you believe related to your personal sense of duty.

4. What are the key characteristics of duty that you prize most?

5. How does your sense of Duty compare with General MacArthur's?

Role of the Army

This is the third of a series of seven lessons on the Army Profession and Officership. This lesson explains and places the organizational structure of the Army in relation to the larger context of the Armed Forces and national security and defense.

The following topics are addressed in this lesson:

- The mission and role of the Army and sister services
- National Security Act of 1947
- Constitutional and legal basis for the Army
- The value of selfless service as part of the Army tradition

The following TLO is supported in whole or in part by this lesson:

- Relate the characteristics of a profession to military service as an officer

Following this lesson you will be able to:

- Explain in general terms, the National Command structure
- Explain the role of the Army, and the Army's mission
- Compare and contrast the role of the Army in relation to its sister organizations

CADET CHECKLIST

___ Go to Blackboard course site for MSL301-Lesson 27 and preview the lesson.

___ Complete the exercise and required readings:

    ___ 1. Read *The American Army* in the textbook.

    ___ 2. Complete the *Role of the Army Question-and-Answer worksheet.* Be sure to bring this to class. *Note: Complete the exercise before completing the next readings.*

    ___ 3. Read *Organizations and Missions* in the textbook.

    ___ 4. Read *National Security Structure* in the textbook.

OPTIONAL

    ___ 1. Read *Backbone vs. Box: The Choice between Principled and Prescriptive Leadership* in the textbook.

    ___ 2. Following class, or at the end of class if time allows, complete either the *Reflection Feedback* or *Summary Review* form.

1	**Exercise Title**	The Role of the Army
2	**Exercise Number**	MSL301_L027_01
3	**Type**	Question-and-Answer worksheet
4	**Notes**	
5	**Purpose**	Introduce the role of the Army to the cadet.
6	**Directions**	

Complete the readings for lesson MSL301_L27. As you read, create a total of seven questions and answers. You need to bring your questions to class where your instructor will call on you to ask questions. Please print or type clearly.

Question/Answer 1:

Question/Answer 2:

Question/Answer 3:

Question/Answer 4:

Question/Answer 5:

Question/Answer 6:

Question/Answer 7:

THE ROLE OF THE ARMY STUDY QUESTIONS

Consider the situation of the world in 1947 and all of the major events transpired in the decade of the 1940's. **What do you think was the driving force behind the reorganization of the national defense structure as accomplished by the National Security Act of 1947?**

In the 21st century, use of military force is no longer as simple as defending our borders against an armed invader. Why is the case, and what are some of the interrelated areas that help determine how we as a nation develop our national military objectives?

Consider the following excerpt from the reading, *"Military forces may be employed to promote and protect national interests across the full range of relationships among nations. These range from peacetime activities, such as disaster relief or nation assistance, to fundamental clashes over ideologies and national objectives."* **What does this mean? Should the Army be doing this? Why or why not?**

When addressing the Reserve Components of the Army, the reading states, *"The reduction in Army strength and the accompanying shift from a forward deployed, to a force projection Army, demands increasingly active cooperation and affiliation between Active and Reserve Components. While the Reserve Components increase the mobilization potential of the Army, they also provide substantial forces to respond to Army missions and contingencies short of wartime mobilization. Reserve Component readiness programs directly support the versatility required of an army that must be able to perform a wide variety of missions or be able to expand on short notice."* **What does this mean? How do you think it will affect you as an Army Officer?**

Organization of the Army

This is the fourth of a series of seven lessons on the Army Profession and Officership. This lesson looks specifically at the composition of the Army and its component parts. The purpose of this lesson is to provide insight on the organization of the Army, while continuing to reinforce the Constitutional and legal basis for the Army, as well as affirming the value of selfless service as part of the Army tradition.

The following topics are addressed in this lesson:

- Organization of the Army from squad through division
- Role and function of the active Army, the Army Reserves and National Guard

The following TLO is supported in whole or in part by this lesson:

- Understand the Army's organization and how the Army runs

Following this lesson you will be able to:

- List the three components of the United States Army
- Describe the composition of the Active Army
- Describe the composition of the Army Reserve
- List the components of the Army National Guard
- Describe the organization of the Army by unit through the division level
- Place the Army in relation to her sister organizations in the military service

CADET CHECKLIST

___ Go to Blackboard course site for MSL301-Lesson 28 and preview the lesson.

___ Complete the required reading and activity:

    ___ 1. Re-read *Organizations and Mission* in lesson 27 in the textbook.

    ___ 2. Complete the pre-class activity—*Organization of the Army Question-and-Answer Worksheet*. You need to create questions and answers based on the reading.

OPTIONAL

    ___ 1. Read FM 7-8, Appendix A on the cadet CD.

    ___ 2. Following class, or at the end of class if time allows, complete either the Reflection Feedback or Summary Review form.

1	**Exercise Title**	Organization of the Army
2	**Exercise Number**	MSL301_L28_01C
3	**Type**	Question-and-Answer worksheet
4	**Notes**	
5	**Purpose**	Cover the component parts of the Army.
6	**Directions**	

Complete the readings for lesson MSL301_L28. As you read, create a total of seven questions and answers. You need to bring your questions to class where your instructor will call on you to ask questions. Be prepared to give the correct answer. Please print or type clearly.

Question/Answer 1:

Question/Answer 2:

Question/Answer 3:

Question/Answer 4:

Question/Answer 5:

Question/Answer 6:

Question/Answer 7:

The Profession of Arms I

This is the fifth of a series of seven lessons on the Army Profession and Officership. This lesson provides the conceptual framework of a profession. The lesson also reviews Huntington's model and clearly explains how Army officership is a profession with regulated duties and expectations.

The following topics are addressed in this lesson:

- The concept of officership as a unique calling in society
- Huntington's model of a profession
- Characteristics of the Profession of Arms

The following TLO is supported in whole or in part by this lesson:

- Relate the characteristics of a profession to military service as an officer

Following this lesson you will be able to:

- Describe Huntington's model of what constitutes a profession
- Differentiate what constitutes the difference between a profession and a job
- Distinguish professions from jobs
- Be able to explain why the military is a profession

CADET CHECKLIST

___ Go to Blackboard course site for MSL301-Lesson 29 and preview the lesson.

___ Complete the required readings and accompanying study questions:

    ___ 1. Read *Officership* in the textbook.

    ___ 2. Scan *Officership as a Profession* in the textbook.

    ___ 3. Read *The Military Profession* and answer the study questions located in this workbook. This reading addresses the concept of a profession, what distinguishes a profession from a job, and how the Officer Corps is considered a profession when compared to other callings in life.

    ___ 4. Scan *On Entering the Military Profession.*

    ___ 5. Preview the Concept Review Question-and-Answer Worksheet.

OPTIONAL

    ___ 1. Read *Expertise Jurisdiction and Legitimacy of the Military.*

    ___ 2. Following class, or at the end of class if time allows, complete either the *Reflection Feedback* or *Summary Review* form.

1	**Exercise Title**	Concept Review Question and Answer
2	**Exercise Number**	MSL301_L29_02C
3	**Type**	Worksheet
4	**Notes**	
5	**Purpose**	To clarify cadet understanding of a profession, and specifically how it may apply to the military profession.

6 Directions

Your instructor will read five questions. Answer in writing below.

1. If you were asked to analyze a group of people with a common line of work, how would you tell whether or not they are in a profession?

2. What constitutes *Professional Expertise?*

3. What relationship does a client have to a professional?

4. What three obligations does the professional have to the client?

5. What two major factors assure that professionals maintain their obligations to their clients?

1	**Exercise Title**	What is a Profession? Exercise	
2	**Exercise Number**	MSL301_L29_03C	
3	**Type**	Small Group Exercise	
4	**Notes**		
5	**Revision Date**	New 3/26/02	
6	**Directions**		*NOTES*

Review the handout with the 5-tier model of a profession. Given the following list of jobs and professions, determine which are, in fact, professions according to the model. You must be able to identify how each of the jobs identified as a profession meets the criteria for each of the five tiers of the model.

In addition, for those jobs not identified as a profession, you must be able to state which criteria the job failed to meet. You will be given 15 minutes to review the list of jobs and reach your conclusion.

Be prepared to discuss your conclusions and defend them in class.

	Medical Doctor	Police Officer	Fire Fighter	Postal Worker	Politician	Military Officer	Teacher	Ordained Minister	Nurse	Lawyer	Sanitation Engineer	Newspaper Editor
EXPERTISE:												
Acquired by prolonged education and experience.												
Separates Layman from professional.												
Measures relative competence within profession.												
Includes basic mechanical skills of craft.												
Extends to leading and managing those engaged in the craft.												
RESPONSIBILITY:												
Practices expertise within the social context.												
Perform service when required by society.												
Goes beyond financial gain/payback.												
Values and ideals of the profession guide members.												
CORPORATENESS:												
Shared sense of unity and consciousness.												
Possesses a written code of ethics.												
Established standards of professional competence.												
CONTROLLED ADMISSION:												
Control over who enters the profession.												
Certification between society and the professional.												
AUTONOMY IN DISCIPLINE AND REGULATION:												
Associated with the professions guarantee of competence.												
Accepted code of ethics.												

PASSES TEST												
DOES NOT PASS TEST												

Y = Meets criteria
N= Does not meet criteria

FIVE-TIER MODEL OF A PROFESSION

(BASED ON HUNTINGTON'S WORK)

FIVE DISTINGUISHING CHARACTERISTICS OF A PROFESSION

Expertise

Acquired by prolonged education and experience.
Separates layman from professional.
Measures relative competence within profession.
Includes basic mechanical skills of craft.
Extends to leading and managing those engaged in the craft.

Responsibility

Practices expertise within the social context.
Perform service when required by society.
Goes beyond financial gain/payback.
Values and ideals of the profession guide members.

Corporateness

Shared sense of unity and consciousness.
Possesses a written code of ethics.
Established standards of professional competence.

Controlled Admission

Control over who enters the profession.
Certification between society and the professional.

Autonomy in Discipline and Regulation

Associated with the professions guarantee of competence.
Accepted code of ethics.

The Profession of Arms II

This is the sixth of a series of seven lessons on the Army Profession and Officership. The intent of this lesson is to acquaint you with the Customs and Traditions that makeup the culture of the Army. This lesson exposes you to the culture of the Army and those customs and traditions that give the Army its rich heritage.

The following topics are addressed in this lesson:

- Importance of Army customs and traditions as aspects of the Army's heritage and organizational culture
- Review and discussion of selected Army customs and traditions

The following TLO is supported in whole or in part by this lesson:

- Relate the characteristics of a profession to military service as an officer

Following this lesson you will be able to:

- Describe the Army Customs of Comradeship, Rank Has Its Privileges, and Welcomes and Farewells
- Describe those actions that the Army considers taboo
- Describe the Army Traditions of Public Service, Achieving the Mission, Leadership, Loyalty, the Officer's Word, Discipline, Readiness, Taking Care of Soldiers, Being a Lady or Gentlemen, Avoiding the Political, and Candor

CADET CHECKLIST

____ Go to Blackboard course site for MSL301-Lesson 30 and preview the lesson.

____ Complete the required readings and exercise:

    ____ 1. Read *Heritage, Customs, and Courtesies of the Army* in the textbook.

    ____ 2. Read—*The Culture of the Army* in the textbook. It provides additional information and broad overview of the importance of imparting knowledge as a tradition.

    ____ 3. Compose three questions and answers on the *Army Profession Customs* worksheet based on the previous readings.

OPTIONAL

    ____ 1. Following class, or at the end of class if time allows, complete either the *Reflection Feedback* or *Summary Review* form.

1	**Exercise Title**	Army Profession Customs
2	**Exercise Number**	MSL301_L30_01C
3	**Type**	Question and Answer worksheet
4	**Notes**	
5	**Purpose**	Cover Army Profession customs and traditions.
6	**Directions**	

Complete the readings for lesson MSL301_L30. As you read, create a total of three questions and answers. Each question must involve the identification and definition of an Army custom or tradition. You need to bring your questions to class where your instructor will call on you to ask questions. Be prepared to give the correct answer. Please print or type clearly.

Question/Answer 1:

Question/Answer 2:

Question/Answer 3:

1	**Exercise Title**	Army Customs and Traditions Analytic Exercise
2	**Exercise Number**	MSL301_L30_02C
3	**Type**	Analytic Exercise
4	**Notes**	
5	**Purpose**	Recognize and identify Army customs and traditions.

6   Directions

Read the attached speech.

Based on your readings and class discussion, identify as many customs and traditions as you can. Circle or hi-lite the passage in the speech, then write in the margin the corresponding custom or tradition.

You have 10 minutes to read the speech and identify the customs and traditions.

Speech	Identify customs & traditions
Given to Officer Basic Course Lieutenants at the Transportation School at Ft. Eustis, Virginia.	
I feel a tinge of regret that I am not young enough to be sitting out there as one of you. You have so many years of challenge and adventure to look forward to. So many of those years are behind me.	_____
Soon you will meet your platoon sergeants, your first sergeants, your other noncommissioned officers and your troops. What do we expect from you as officers, commanders, leaders?	_____
We expect of you unassailable personal integrity and the highest of morals. We expect you to maintain the highest state of personal appearance. We expect you to be fair—to be consistent—to have dignity, but not aloofness—to have compassion and understanding—to treat each soldier as an individual, with individual problems.	_____
And we expect you to have courage—the courage of your convictions—the courage to stand up and be counted—to defend your men when they have followed your orders, even when your orders were in error—to assume the blame when you are wrong.	_____

Speech (cont'd)	Identify customs & traditions
We expect you to stick out your chin and say, "This man is worthy of promotion, and I want him promoted." And we expect you to have even greater courage and say, "This man is not qualified and he will be promoted over my dead body!" Gentlemen, I implore you, do not promote a man because he is a nice guy, because he has a wife and five kids, because he has money problems, because he has a bar bill. If he is not capable of performing the duties of his grade, do not do him and us the injustice of advancing him in grade. When he leaves you, or you leave him, he becomes someone else's problem!	_____
Gentlemen, we expect of you to have courage in the face of danger. Many of you will soon be in Vietnam where there are no safe rear echelons. During your tour, opportunities will arise for you to display personal courage and leadership. Opportunities could arise from which you may emerge as heroes. A hero is an individual who is faced with an undesirable situation and employs whatever means are at his disposal to make the situation tenable or to nullify or negate it.	
Do not display recklessness and expose yourself and your men to unnecessary risks that will reduce their normal chance of survival. This will only shake their confidence in your judgement.	
Now gentlemen, you know what we expect from you. What can you expect from us?	
From a few of us, you can expect antagonism, a "Prove yourself" attitude.	
From a few of us who had the opportunity to be officers, didn't have the guts and motivation to except the challenge, you can expect resentment.	
From a few of us old-timers, you can expect tolerance.	
But from most of us you can expect loyalty to your position, devotion to our cause, admiration for your honest effort—courage to match your courage, guts to match your guts—endurance to match your endurance—motivation to match your motivation—esprit to match your esprit—a desire for achievement to match your desire for achievement.	

Speech (cont'd)	Identify customs & traditions
You can expect a love of God, a love of country, and a love of duty to match your love of God, your love of country, and your love of duty.	_____

You can expect a love of God, a love of country, and a love of duty to match your love of God, your love of country, and your love of duty.

We won't mind the heat if you sweat with us. We won't mind the cold if you shiver with us. And when our cigarettes are gone, we won't mind quitting smoking after your cigarettes are gone.

Gentlemen, you don't accept us, we were here first. We accept you, and when we do, you'll know. We won't beat drums, or carry you off the drill field on our shoulders. But, maybe a company party, we'll raise a canteen cup of beer and say, "Lieutenant, you're O. K." Just like that.

Remember one thing. Very few noncommissioned officers were awarded stripes without showing somebody something, sometime, somewhere. If your platoon sergeant is mediocre, if he is slow to assume responsibility, if he shies away from you, maybe sometime not too long ago someone refused to trust him, someone failed to support his decisions, someone shot him down when he was right. Internal wounds heal slowly; internal scars fade more slowly.

Your orders appointing you as officers in the United States Army appointed you to command. No orders, no letters, no insignia of rank, can appoint you as leaders. Leadership is an intangible thing; leaders are made, they are not born. Leadership is developed within yourselves.

You do not wear leadership on your sleeves, on your shoulders, on your caps or on your calling cards. Be you lieutenants or generals, we're the guys you've got to convince and we'll meet you more than halfway.

You are leaders in an Army in which we have served for so many years, and you will help us defend the country we have loved for so many years.

I wish you happiness, luck and success in the exciting and challenging years that lie ahead.

May God bless you all!

Sergeant Major John Stepanek

Warrior Ethos

This is the last of a series of seven lessons on the Army Profession and Officership. This lesson builds on earlier lessons focused on the Army Profession and Officership, and the concepts of Honor, Duty, and Country. The theme of this lesson is on the character and characteristics of the warrior, as well as how you can recognize and model the warrior ethos.

The following topics are addressed in this lesson:

- The characteristics of the warrior ethos
- Characteristics of the Army warrior
- Personal goals as they relate to the Army Profession

The following TLO is supported in whole or in part by this lesson:

- Relate the characteristics of a profession to military service as an officer

Following this lesson you will be able to:

- Describe the Army Warrior Ethos
- Distinguish between leaders who possess the Army Warrior Ethos and those who do not

CADET CHECKLIST

____ Go to Blackboard course site for MS301-Lesson 31 and preview the lesson.

____ Complete the required readings and exercise:

    ____ 1. Read excerpt from *Black Hawk Down* in the textbook.

    ____ 2. Read *Character and the Warrior Ethos* in the textbook. As you read this, consider the last six lessons on Officership.

    ____ 3. Read *Medal of Honor* in the textbook.

    ____ 4. Complete the *Characteristics of a Warrior* worksheet. As you select a warrior, consider Medal of Honor awardees.

OPTIONAL

    ____ 1. Read *A Message to Garcia: Leading Soldiers in Moral Mayhem* in the textbook.

    ____ 2. Following class, or at the end of class if time allows, complete either the *Reflection Feedback* or *Summary Review* form.

1	**Exercise Title**	Characteristics of a Warrior
2	**Exercise Number**	MSL301_L31_01C
3	**Type**	Worksheet
4	**Notes**	If you are having trouble making a selection, refer to the List of Medal of Honor awardees in your textbook.
5	**Purpose**	Raise cadets' awareness of warrior characteristics.
6	**Directions**	

Directions

Use the following guidelines to prepare a brief that you can present in class. You can browse the web, use an encyclopedia, or a reference work to fill out the worksheet.

Select a warrior you admire. The warrior you select can be an historic person or a fictional character.

1. Name of Warrior.

2. Identify the historic or fictional era when the warrior lived.

3. Identify the region or nation where the warrior lived.

4. Identify the three actions/deeds of the warrior.

5. What are five key characteristics of a warrior?

6. To what extent do the general characteristics of a warrior relate to the specific characteristics of the warrior you selected to research? Explain how your warrior fulfills the definition of a warrior.

7. Write a brief summary description of the warrior you selected.

8. Of the warrior characteristics you identified, do you possess any of those characteristics? If so, which ones?

9. Which characteristics do you most admire in the warrior you selected?

10. Of all the characteristics of the warrior ethos, is there one you can and want to achieve? How will you begin to work at achieving your goal?

Officership Case Study I

This is the first case study in a set of five case studies on the evolution of the Army. The intent of this lesson is to have you gain familiarity with the historic context in which the U.S. became involved in the Vietnam Conflict, to identify the policies and practices of the Vietnam Conflict, and the lessons that need to be learned from that era. In addition, you will learn about the Threads of Continuity, the Six Imperatives, and how they can be applied so as to recognize and guide an organization in change.

The following topics are addressed in this lesson:

- The history of American involvement
- The policies and practices of the Vietnam Conflict
- The conduct of the Officer corps
- The Threads of Continuity
- The Six Imperatives

The following TLO is supported in whole or in part by this lesson:

- Institute change in an organization

Following this lesson you will be able to:

- Identify the key elements needed to institute a change within an organization
- Analyze the evolution of the Army using the Threads of Continuity

CADET CHECKLIST

____ Go to Blackboard course site for MS301-Lesson 32 and preview the lesson.

____ Complete the required readings:

    ____ 1. Read *Vietnam's Forgotten Lessons* in the textbook.

    ____ 2. Review *Policies and Practices of the Vietnam War,* in this workbook.

    ____ 3. Read *The Threads of Continuity—The Six Imperatives,* in this workbook.

    ____ 4. Preview *The Threads of Continuity Lessons Learned* Exercise in this workbook.

OPTIONAL

    ____ 1. Screen *A History of Vietnam* (PBS), Part 1, as available.

    ____ 2. Read *Impressions of an Infantryman in Vietnam* in the textbook.

    ____ 3. Following class, or at the end of class if time allows, complete either the *Reflection Feedback* or *Summary Review* form.

1	**Exercise Title**	Threads of Continuity Lessons Learned Exercise
2	**Exercise Number**	MSL301_L32_02C
3	**Type**	Analytic worksheet
4	**Notes**	
5	**Purpose**	Recognize the negative impact that a set of policies and practices had on the military during the Vietnam conflict.

Directions

6

On the attached sheet is a series of questions organized by Threads of Continuity.

Your instructor will assign each group a question. You need to work from the Threads of Continuity handout and the *Policies and Practices of the Vietnam War* reading.

The *Policies and Practices of the Vietnam War* gives you background information and explains the rationale for how the policy or practice came in to being.

Your task is to analyze the policy or practice in terms of the Threads of Continuity and determine how that practice or policy became a risk or liability to the military. You also need to recommend needed change.

Be prepared to defend your analysis and recommendations.

LESSONS LEARNED—THREADS OF CONTINUITY—POLICIES IMPLEMENTED DURING VIETNAM

WAR FIGHTING DOCTRINE

1. What is wrong with combat tours being one year in length?

2. How well did the "Graduated Response strategy" work?

3. Were the command tours of only 6 months effective?

4. What was the impact of setting objectives in terms of body count? What was the result of false reporting?

5. How did Restricted Areas impact the conduct of the war?

INTEGRATION OF RESERVE FORCES

6. No reserve call-up. What was the impact of having a no reserve call-up strategy?

EMPOWERMENT OF THE NCO CORPS

7. The NCO Corps was used to train 90-Day wonders. What were the advantages and disadvantages of the 90-day wonders?

QUALITY OF PEOPLE

8. Project 100,000; What kind of soldiers do we need to fight our nation's war? Does Johnson's 100,000 fit that description? Discuss the "quality of people."

LEADER DEVELOPMENT

9. What was the impact of having no Commander-in-Chief?

FORCE STRUCTURE

10. What was the impact of having no unity of command in Vietnam?

CONTINUOUS MODERNIZATION

11. How was technology used? Was it effective? How could it have been more effective?

INSTITUTIONAL VALUES

12. How do you reestablish the Army values once they have been lost? Were they lost during the Vietnam conflict? How do you train officers/NCOs to emulate the Army values? (Loyalty, Duty, Respect, Selfless Service, Honesty, Integrity, and Courage).

POLICIES AND PRACTICES OF THE VIETNAM WAR

Listed below are the Administrative Policies and Practices that had a profound effect on the war in Vietnam. Included with each one is the rationale of why they were implemented.

In class cadets need to analyze why each of these had an adverse impact on the conduct of the war.

Combat Tours One Year in Length—Soldiers in Vietnam were with their unit for exactly one year and then they went back to the U.S. In both World War II and Korea, soldiers stayed with their unit until the war was over or their entire unit rotated back to the U.S.

Rationale: *There were two reasons why this was implemented. (1) During both World War II and Korea soldiers returned to the U.S. after those conflicts with a very high rate of what is called today Post Traumatic Stress Disorder (PTSD). (2) With soldiers constantly returning from Vietnam the intention was to minimize any public outcry to "Bring our soldiers home"—as there had been during the Korean Conflict.*

Combat Command Tours Six Months in Length—Officers commanded units for exactly six months and then did a staff assignment for six months.

Rationale: *Since it was assumed that the war was going to be short in duration, this policy intended to allow as many commanders as possible to get command time in combat, thus preparing them for the "big one" (war) in Europe. In addition, combat command tours looked great on efficiency reports, thus these tours made their military record look better, AND got them promoted more quickly.*

"90-day wonders"—Program intended to produce officers in 90 days through a very rigorous training program. (There was also a program similar to this that accelerated the training time for NCOs.) Upon completion, officers were sent straight to Vietnam and took over as platoon leaders in combat, and combat support units. The first 90-day wonders started arriving in Vietnam in 1969.

Rationale: *After the first couple years of the war, there was a shortage of trained Officers, and NCOs for that matter, in combat and combat support units. Heavy casualties, combined with the fact that many elected not to return to Vietnam for a second tour, forced officials to find a program to produce quality officers and NCOs quickly.*

Restricted Areas—Certain areas were off limits to U.S forces. U.S. troops were not authorized to attack those areas, just like the Air Force was not authorized to bomb certain areas. In some cases, the enemy would attack out of a restricted area, and then when they started losing the battle, they would retreat back into a restricted area.

Rationale: During the Korean Conflict U.S. troops had gotten too close to the Chinese border. This had provoked the Chinese to enter that war. In Vietnam, there were several restricted areas near the Chinese border. The rationale was that the U.S. did not want a repeat of what happened during the Korean Conflict. In Cambodia, the President of Cambodia told the U.S. that there were no NVA in his country, and therefore there was no reason for U.S. forces to cross his borders. The Johnson administration complied, since they did not want to de-stabilize Cambodia.

Project 100,000—President Johnson lowered the minimum intellectual and physical standards for entry into the military. About 300,000 men came into the military as part of this program. Many could not read or write. The first soldiers from this program started to arrive in Vietnam in 1966. Many would stay in the Army long after Vietnam.

Rationale: *President Johnson as part of his "Great Society" program designed to "rehabilitate the sub-terranean poor" allowed underprivileged and unemployed youths to join the service.*

No Reserve Call-up—Since the assumption was that the war was going to be short, President Johnson believed there was no need to call up the Reserve Forces (Army Guard and Army Reserve), despite there being a wealth of experience in both organizations.

Rationale: *President Johnson believed the Active Duty Army had enough troops to accomplish the mission in Vietnam. In addition, a reserve call-up would require Congressional approval and bring the conflict to the forefront of the American public. President Johnson did not want that to happen since that could jeopardize his "Great Society" agenda.*

No Commander-In-Chief (CINC)—Even though General Westmoreland was in command of Military Assistance Command-Vietnam (MAC-V), he was NOT in command of all the forces in the region. Navy pilots flying bombing missions off carriers in the Gulf of Tonkin reported directly to Headquarters, U.S. Pacific Command in Hawaii. U.S. Air Force B-52 aircrews flying bombing missions in Vietnam still reported to the Strategic Air Command (SAC) in Omaha, Nebraska.

Rationale: *No clear rationale. During WWII, Generals MacArthur and Eisenhower were in command of all the forces in their respective theaters of war. However, during the 1960s, 70s, and for much of the 80s, no service wanted to be subordinate to a commander from a different service. Inter-service rivalries were very intense during this period.*

"Graduated Response"—This is a "strategy" where the U.S. would bomb North Vietnam for several days or weeks then stop. Often these attacks would come in response to some North Vietnamese action or attack. The U.S. then would gradually increase the size and magnitude of its attacks.

Rationale: *Secretary of Defense Robert McNamara convinced President Johnson that this strategy would force the North Vietnamese to negotiate a peace settlement. McNamara essentially used the same strategy during the Cuban Missile Crisis in 1962 to force the Soviet Union to remove their missiles from Cuba.*

"Body Count" and False Reporting—In a "war of attrition" (meaning you kill so many of the enemy that they will eventually give up), a way to determine whether or not you are winning is to count the number of enemy dead bodies after each battle. Since the NVA often carried their dead off the battlefield, whenever possible, the "blood trails" left behind as enemy wounded retreated were often reported as enemy dead too. This practice along with other inconsequential statistical requirements lead to many units simply reporting what higher headquarters wanted to hear, and not the truth.

Rationale: *SECDEF McNamara was a fanatical believer in quantitative analysis as the solution to any problem, even Vietnam. To justify the number of troops, planes, bombs, and tanks in Vietnam, he had to come up with a way to show that we were winning the war. "Body count" was just one of many methods used to "define" success.*

THE THREADS OF CONTINUITY—THE SIX IMPERATIVES

The *Threads of Continuity* are used by the cadet to identify and to trace the critical phases of the transformation of the Army and the Officer Corps from Vietnam to the Present. These threads are used as the framework by which the student can evaluate and critique the Army anywhere along the transformation process. It is used to trace the evolution of the Army and the responsibilities, influences, successes, and failures of the Officer Corps.

Listed below are the nine threads of continuity including some questions/issues that the Army has faced in the past, present, and future.

1. Quality of People: Whom do we want in our Army? Does it represent the nation as a whole? (Example: If the nation is 19% Hispanic, should the Army also be approximately 19% Hispanic?) What percent of the Army should women comprise? What should the education requirement be to enter the Army? What percent of non-high school graduates is acceptable? Does every officer need a college education? How can the Army attract quality people when the economy is doing well?

2. War Fighting Doctrine: Doctrine is how we as an Army THINK about fighting. It is our philosophy on how we want to fight. It is our guiding principles so to speak. What happens if the guiding principles are wrong? Or outdated? Does new technology change our doctrine?

3. Force Structure: How many divisions does the Army need? What type of divisions do we need? (Armor, Infantry, Light Infantry, or Medium sized?) Important: What kind of units should comprise the Guard and Reserve? What jobs can be contracted out or done by civilians?

4. Training: What kind of training is needed? What subjects should be taught to our future officers? How often should our officers and NCOs attend Army schools? What should be taught at these schools? How do you know when you have it right?

5. Continuous Modernization: What new equipment is needed? How do you know when a piece of equipment is obsolete? With limited budgets, how can the Army afford the new equipment it wants? What piece of equipment is needed the most?

6. Leader Development: How many years does it take to produce a quality officer? (Two, three, or four years?) What does it take to attract and retain a quality leader?

Empowerment of the NCO Corps: The NCOs are the backbone of the Army. The better our NCOs are, the better the Army is. The Army wants to empower the NCOs to be able to give them a mission and let them determine the best method to execute the mission. When the quality of the NCOs drops, then empowerment suffers. The NCOs are also the primary trainers of new lieutenants when they arrive at their first unit.

Integration of Reserve Forces: The Reserve forces (Army Guard and Reserve) must be integrated into the Total Army. What are their strengths and weaknesses? What missions can they perform best? What type of units should they consist of? How does the Army know if they are ready to perform their wartime missions? Keep in mind that politics plays a major factor in their training, composition, and deployment?

Institutional Values: The Army is a value-based organization. At times in the history of the Army this has not always been the case. How do you reestablish these values once they have been lost? How do you train officers/NCOs to emulate the Army values? (Loyalty, Duty, Respect, Selfless Service, Honesty, Integrity, and Courage.)

   NOTE: General Carl Vuono, Chief-of-Staff of the Army 1987-1989, took the Nine Threads of Continuity and called them the "Six Imperatives." General Vuono called them, *"a beacon to steer us through the uncertain future in the next century"*: Quality, Doctrine, Force Structure, Training, Modernization, and Leader Development.

Officership Case Study II: The Hollow Army of the 1970's

This is the second case study in a set of five case studies on the evolution of the Army. This lesson focuses on the post Vietnam challenges and the leaders who tackled the problems, and rebuilt the Army. This lesson covers the state of the Army in the early 1970's after Vietnam. The lesson covers the character and vision of outstanding officers, including Creighton Abrams, who led the Army out of what has been described as the Army's darkest period since the days of General Washington at Valley Forge.

The following topics are addressed in this lesson:

- Challenges of leadership in the post-Vietnam environment
- The framework for the changes that would take place under the new Chief-of-Staff
- Key people involved in rebuilding the Army

The following TLO is supported in whole or in part by this lesson:

- Integrate military history into education of officers

Following this lesson you will be able to:

- Describe the conduct of officers in the post Vietnam era
- Identify the challenges facing the post Vietnam Army
- Summarize the major changes initiated by General Abrams in the post Vietnam Army

CADET CHECKLIST

___ Go to Blackboard course site for MSL301-Lesson 33 and preview the lesson.

___ Complete the required readings:

    ___ 1. Read *To Change an Army* in the textbook.

    ___ 2. Read *The Hollow Army* in the textbook.

    ___ 3. Read *The Renaissance* in the textbook.

    ___ 4. Preview *Army in Anguish Branstorming* exercise. Review the problems facing the Army in the early 1970's.

OPTIONAL

    ___ 1. Following class, or at the end of class if time allows, complete either the *Reflection Feedback* or *Summary Review* form.

1	Exercise Title	Army in Anguish Brainstorming
2	Exercise Number	MSL301_L33_01C
3	Type	Brainstorming worksheet
4	Notes	
5	Purpose	Recognize how strong, visionary leadership can change an organization for the better.

6	Directions

Assume the information on the attached sheet is the result of a recent survey on a Fortune 500 company known as BDC, Inc. (Also known by the employees as Broken Down Company Inc.) BDC once had a reputation as one of the best automobile factories in the world.

You have been tasked by the CEO to brainstorm some ideas on how to fix this company and get it back on the top of the Fortune 500 list. The CEO wants your preliminary analysis in the next 20 minutes.

Your instructor will break the class in to small teams. Your team has 15 minutes to brainstorm your analysis, then five minutes to report your recommendations for change.

Working from the information on the attached sheet, come up with three alternatives for each problem. Then organize the list of problems in terms of priority for action. What is most important to address first? Lay out an idea of what to do first, second, where there are dependencies, and where to put the resources you have.

Assume you have limited or flat resources. Do not assume that you can throw money at these problems in order to solve them.

Note that these were just some of the problems facing General Abrams when he took over as the Chief of Staff of the Army in 1972.

Note: The data points in bold below each problem are taken from the Washington Post National Report *entitled "Army in Anguish," (1972) and Robert Scale's book* Certain Victory.

ARMY IN ANGUISH—SURVEY RESULTS AND DATA POINTS

1. Drug use in the workplace and on the job. Mostly marijuana but also starting to see some employees addicted to heroin.
   Data Point: *Early 1970's, 40% of the Army in Europe confessed to drug use, mostly hashish. A little over 7% were addicted to heroin.*

2. Employee crime and absenteeism.
   Data Point: *In Germany, 12% of the soldiers were charged with serious offenses.*

3. Employee housing is substandard. Paint falling of the ceilings, holes in exterior walls, kitchen appliances defective, and numerous plumbing problems.

4. Racial Problems. Numerous reports off whites vs. blacks in gang-related violence.

5. Junior and Mid-level executives fleeing in large numbers to other car companies. Exit surveys from these individuals say that BDC lacks pride, and it is not a professional organization.

6. Cars being produced are almost obsolete. Surveys show consumers lack faith in the BDC product.
   Data Point: *1973 Harris Survey Poll revealed that the American public ranked the military slightly above sanitation workers in regard to respect.*

7. A large majority of the workers on the assembly line are <u>not</u> High School graduates.
   Data Point: *Of the soldiers entering the Army in the early 1970's, 40% had no high school diploma and 41% were Category IV (lowest mental aptitude category).*

8. Supervisors on the assembly line are not trained, nor are there any schools to send them to for training.

9. Personnel Report says that BDC has too many staff employees at corporate, regional, and district offices. Report suggests that many of these offices duplicate the work done at other levels within the company.

10. Survey says BDC is having a hard time attracting new employees.
    Data Point: *By 1974, The Army was short 20,000 soldiers below authorizations and missed their recruiting goal by 11%.*

11. Survey says BDC is woefully inadequate in the area of training. Three examples are cited in the survey:
    a. No training program to improve the performance of the workforce.
    b. No feedback system in place for good ideas to reach management.
    c. No "planning cell" to think about the future of the company.

Officership Case Study III: Transformation

This is the third case study in a set of five case studies on the evolution of the Army. This lesson draws a direct connection between the success of the Army and the doctrine and training philosophy. The lesson covers the critical role of the NCOs and describes the "Big Five" weapons program and how this has contributed to success in battle. Special emphasis is placed on the basic principles of General Starry's AirLand Battle doctrine.

The following topics are addressed in this lesson:

- The transformation of the Army
- The critical role NCOs play in our Army
- The "Big Five" weapons program

The following TLO is supported in whole or in part by this lesson:

- Integrate military history into education of officers

Following this lesson you will be able to:

- Describe the change in training doctrine that occurred with creation of the Combat Training Centers (CTCs)
- Explain the importance of the resurgence of the NCO corps during the period

CADET CHECKLIST

___ Go to Blackboard course site for MSL301-Lesson 34 and review the lesson.

___ Complete the required readings and exercise:

   ___ 1. Read *The Big Five* in the textbook.

   ___ 2. Scan *The U.S. Army in the Gulf War* in the textbook.

   ___ 3. Complete the *Army in Transition* Question-and-Answer Worksheet in the workbook. As part of this activity, you need to construct questions and answers from the readings. Be sure to bring your filled-in answer worksheet to class.

   ___ 4. Complete the Key Players Worksheet in the workbook.

OPTIONAL

   ___ 1. Following class, or at the end of class if time allows, complete either the *Reflection Feedback* or *Summary Review* form.

   ___ 2. Reread *Black Hawk Down* in Lesson 31.

   ___ 3. Review *The Whirlwind War: The United States Army in Operation Desert Shield and Desert Storm*, gen. eds. Frank N. Schubert and Theresa L. Kraus.

1	**Exercise Title**	Army in Transition
2	**Exercise Number**	MSL301_L34_01C
3	**Type**	Question-and-Answer worksheet
4	**Notes**	
5	**Purpose**	Identify a series of changes that had a significant and positive impact on the post-Vietnam era Army.

6	**Directions**

Complete the readings for lesson MSL301_L34. As you read, create a total of five questions and answers. Your questions and answers and those from each cadet will be added to a pool for the class exercise. Please print or type clearly.

Question/Answer 1:

Question/Answer 2:

Question/Answer 3:

Question/Answer 4:

Question/Answer 5:

Question/Answer 6:

Question/Answer 7:

Question/Answer 8:

GENERAL STARRY'S AIRLAND BATTLE DOCTRINE STUDY QUESTIONS

1. Based on the lessons of the October 1973 war, the "Active Defense" was based on weapons effects, exchange ratios, and the return to the "firepower-attrition" warfare. There was very little emphasis on leader initiative. It also focused on defense, inside of the offense. (Hence the name "Active Defense")

2. General Starry, walking the potential battlefields, realized that while numbers count, battles usually go to the side that sometime during the battle, gains and maintains the initiative until the battle is over. (This was something the Israelis had done in 1973.)

So, General Starry wrote the new FM 100-5 to describe a totally new doctrine that the Army must have to defeat a numerically superior, high tech opponent. This is what he came up with.

- Leadership is an element of combat power equal to firepower and maneuver.
- Success is based on the tenets of initiative, depth, agility and synchronization.
- Must defeat enemy second and third echelon forces deep in their own territory, while simultaneously destroying the enemy's first echelon forces.
- To do these deep attacks, the doctrine called for deep artillery fires, Close Air Support (CAS), electronic warfare, and deep attacks by attack helicopters and fast moving armored forces.

STUDY QUESTIONS

Question: Why, given this method of warfare, do you think General Starry placed so much emphasis on leadership?

Question: What does General Starry mean by "synchronization"?

Question: What does General Starry mean when he uses the term attacking the enemy 2d and 3d echelons? Why does he want to attack them early in battle?

Question: How does an Army successfully execute deep attacks?

MG DON STARRY'S NEW ARMOR TACTICS (1974)

Instructions: Compare and contrast the guidance of MG Don Starry, then commandant of the Armor School at Ft. Knox, Kentucky, put out in 1974, versus his AirLand Battle doctrine for FM 100-5, put out in 1982.

MG Starry was one of the few U.S. Army officers who visited the battlefields in the Middle East shortly after the October 1973 Arab-Israeli war.

Based on the lessons learned and what he saw, he concluded that a modern battlefield, whether Europe or elsewhere, would be characterized by massive numbers of highly lethal anti-tank and anti-aircraft weapons. Furthermore, MG Starry posited, the U.S. forces would be outnumbered from the start, and this would require new priorities for armor tactics. This would mean—

1. Detecting and identifying the enemy main body at the *maximum* possible distances

2. Teaching tank gunners to fire fast first

3. Controlling and distributing anti-tank fires so that ammunition is available to engage succeeding enemy echelons

4. Delivering suppressive fires from "overwatch"

5. Flying Army aircraft nap of the earth or as close to the ground as possible to use terrain and vegetation as cover and concealment without limiting mobility

6. Destroying enemy air defense weapons

7. Using reverse slopes as avenues of approach for attack and counterattack

8. Fighting with skill at night and in periods of reduced visibility

9. Using highly reliable tactical communications

10. Employing highly flexible, responsive, and self-sufficient logistical support

---

Herbert, Paul H. (1988). Deciding What Has to Be Done: General William E. DePuy and the 1976 Edition of FM 100-5, Operations. *Leavenworth Papers #16.* Fort Leavenworth, Kansas.

THE KEY PLAYERS

This section will give students some questions to focus their research on the four generals that turned the Army around in its darkest days following the Vietnam War. Each portion begins with a synopsis of the jobs they held during Vietnam and shortly after the war.

GENERAL CREIGHTON "ABE" ABRAMS

Served as Deputy Commander to General Westmoreland, Commander Military Assistance Command-Vietnam (MAC-V). Became the Commander, MAC-V from 1970–1972. Served as Chief-of-Staff, U.S. Army from 1972–1974. For more information—http://www.army.mil/cmh-pg/books/cg&csa/Abrams-CW.htm

Question: Perhaps his greatest accomplishment had to do with the Reserve Forces. What was the change and how does it affect our Army and nation today?

Question: General Abrams was also the Chief of Staff when the draft ended and we started the All Volunteer Army. Describe some of the challenges the Army faced going to an all volunteer force.

GENERAL WILLIAM DEPUY

Served as G-3 (Operations Officer) in the First Infantry Division in Vietnam and later commanded a Brigade in the same division in Vietnam. Selected by General Abrams to be the first commander of TRADOC. For more information—http://www.tradoc.army.mil

Question: General DePuy was selected by General Abrams to command the newly formed Training and Doctrine Command (TRADOC). What does that organization do, and what were the challenges that face TRADOC in the early 70s?

GENERAL DON STARRY

Served as Commander, 11th Armored Cavalry Regiment in Vietnam. Later he would work under both General DePuy and General Abrams. He would later command TRADOC after General DePuy retired.

Question: What did General Starry learn from his visits to Golan Heights right after the Yom Kippor War? How did this information impact our doctrine in Europe.

GENERAL EDWARD "SHY" MEYER

Served as Brigade commander in the 1st Cavalry Division in Vietnam. Prior to that he worked with then Chief-of-Staff Harold Johnson just prior to the Vietnam buildup. Selected as the youngest Chief-of-Staff of the Army by President Carter.

Question: One of the great Army experiments during Meyer's time as Chief of Staff of the Army was the COHORT units. What were they and what were their advantages and disadvantages?

Officership Case Study IV

This is the fourth case study in a set of five case studies on the evolution of the Army. Whereas the earlier lessons in this set focused on the negative impact of policies and practices during the Vietnam era, the struggles of Army leaders to overcome a variety of challenges, and the changes that visionary leaders gradually implemented, this lesson shows the results. The work that was done paid off—the Army has transformed itself. The initiatives begun by General Abrams in the early 1970s are witnessed in the success in the Gulf War.

The following topics are addressed in this lesson:

- The fruition of initiatives started in the early 1970s
- The Threads of Continuity
- Clausewitz's Trinity: The relationship among the people, nation, and the Army
- The conduct of the officer corps

The following TLO is supported in whole or in part by this lesson:

- Integrate military history into education of officers

Following this lesson you will be able to:

- Compare and contrast how the Gulf War was conducted versus the Vietnam War
- Use the Threads of Continuity to describe some of the initiatives begun in the 1970s that contributed to the success of the Gulf War
- Describe how the Combat Training Centers (CTC) contributed to the victory in the Gulf War

CADET CHECKLIST

___ Go to Blackboard course site for MSL301-Lesson 35 and review the lesson.

___ Complete the required readings:

    ___ 1. Read *Operation Desert Shield/Desert Storm: Chronology of Events.*

    ___ 2. Review *The U.S. Army in the Gulf War* from lesson 34.

    ___ 3. Review *The Big Five* from lesson 34.

OPTIONAL

    ___ 1. Scan *Army Mission Essential Tasks* in FM3-0 Operations, paragraphs 1-5 through 1-23, located on the cadet CD

    ___ 2. Following class, or at the end of class if time allows, complete either the *Reflection Feedback* or *Summary Review* form.

Officership Case Study V: Into the 21st Century

This is the last case study in a set of five case studies on the evolution of the Army. This lesson identifies a number of the post-Cold War challenges and the activities of the current Army as it undergoes transformation. The purpose of this lesson is to describe the challenges and risks of the 21st century, and to generate ideas as to how risks can be minimized and opportunities seized.

The following topics are addressed in this lesson:

- The conduct and effect of the post-Cold War downsizing
- The evolving missions of the Army
- Ongoing Army transition and modernization initiatives

The following TLO is supported in whole or in part by this lesson:

- Integrate military history into education of officers

Following this lesson you will be able to:

- Identify the types of current missions facing the Army today
- Describe the challenges facing the post-Cold War Army
- Summarize an officer's unique responsibilities to the future of the Army

CADET CHECKLIST

___ Go to Blackboard course site for MSL301-Lesson 36 and preview the lesson.

___ Complete the required readings:

    ___ 1. Read *The Downsized Warrior* in the textbook.

    ___ 2. Review the *Brainstorming Guidelines,* located on the cadet CD

    ___ 3. Preview the *Army in the 21st Century* worksheet you will use as part of the in-class exercise.

OPTIONAL

    ___ 1. Following class, or at the end of class if time allows, complete either the *Reflection Feedback* or *Summary Review* form.

    ___ 2. Following class, or at the end of class if time allows, complete the Cadet Evaluation of Instructor form. As you respond, consider all of the lessons and related experiences that made up this module, The Army Profession: Officership.

1	**Exercise Title**	Army in the 21st Century Worksheet
2	**Exercise Number**	MSL301_L36_01C
3	**Type**	Worksheet
4	**Notes**	
5	**Purpose**	To consider the future of the Army.
6	**Direction**	

In the first part of the lesson the class brainstormed the challenges facing the Army in the 21st century.

Select one of the items from the list the class brainstormed.

Identify the item _____

Now answer the following questions:

1. Is there a negative impact? _____

2. If so, what is it? _____

3. If there is a negative impact, what is the scope of the impact? The next 1–3 years? In the next 10–15 years? _____
_____

4. Is there an opportunity associated with this item? _____

5. Describe the opportunity. _____
_____

6. Identify three actions that need to be taken now in order manage whatever risk is involved. ____
_____
_____

7. From the list on the board, what are the three items you consider most critical to be addressed as soon as possible? _____
_____
_____

8. What are the likely consequences if no action is taken? _____
_____
_____

Notes: _____
_____
_____
_____
_____
_____
_____

RESOURCES

URLS ACCESSED DURING THE COURSE:

Blackboard: http://rotc.blackboard.com/

HOOAH 4 Health: http://hooah4health.com

HOOAH 4 YOU:
http://hooah4health.com/4You/default.htm

Health Goals Checklist:
http://www.hooah4health.com/4You/hgoalsadultsurvey.asp

Food Pyramid Game:
http://www.hooah4health.com/body/pyramidinteractive.htm

Learning Style Inventory:
http://www.metamath.com//lsweb/dvclearn.htm

Learning Style Inventory Survey:
http://www.metamath.com//multiple/multiple choice questions.cgi

General Creighton Abrams
http://www.army.mil/cmh-pg/books/cgicsa/Abrams.CW.htm

General William Depuy
http://www.tradoc.army.mil

MacArthur Speech-Duty, honor, country
http://www.west-point.org/real/macarthur_address.html

STANDARD FORMS

CADET EVALUATION OF INSTRUCTOR

Research indicates that providing students the opportunity to give feedback helps improve the quality of the lessons. The purpose of this questionnaire is to help improve the quality of teaching and learning. This evaluation is independent of the university-wide course survey. Please answer each item honestly and thoughtfully.

Instructor Appraisal		Please choose one response and mark with an X.				
Based on your perceptions, indicate how strongly you agree or disagree with each of the following statements:		Strongly Agree	Somewhat Agree	Disagree	Strongly Disagree	Not Applicable
1	The instructor's knowledge of the subject and discipline is excellent.					
2	Papers, tests, and written assignments are graded and returned in a timely manner.					
3	The instructor's presentations are organized, clear, and understandable.					
4	The types of instructional activities/tools (PowerPoint lectures, small group exercises, and discussions) used by the instructor are helpful.					
5	The instructor is able to give more explanations, illustrations and references when needed.					
6	The instructor is enthusiastic about the subject.					
7	The instructor encouraged me to express myself and to ask questions.					
8	The instructor's responses to my questions are helpful.					
9	The instructor is available to provide extra help when needed.					
10	The instructor is genuinely interested in whether or not I succeed.					

REFLECTION FEEDBACK

Please respond to the following four questions:

1. Based on today's class session, what is the most significant observation or insight you had?

2. Is this a new observation or insight, or is this more of an affirmation of something you already understand?

3. Explain why this observation or insight is significant?

4. How will this new insight affect what you do or think?

SUMMARY REVIEW

A summary review (SR) is a professional discussion of an event, focused on performance standards. An SR enables cadets to discover for themselves what worked, what failed to work, and how to improve the situation next time. This is a tool for continuous improvement. It gives the cadet the opportunity to reflect upon any insight, observations, or lessons learned from the activity or event.

PURPOSE

To review and reinforce learning.

DIRECTIONS

1. Summarize in writing what you have learned.

2. Identify one action you intend to take as a result of the lesson (whether readings, in-class game, or discussion).

3. Hand in the completed SR to the instructor before you leave the classroom.